1 C'est Gaston!

Dessine-toi.

C'est moi. Je m'appelle ....

2 Comment tu t'appelles?

3 Les salutations.

(Page 27)

4 Que disent-ils?

5 La journée.

Bonjour, mademoiselle!
Bonjour, Thierry!
ÉCOLE JULES FERRY

Salut, Lucile!
Salut, Thierry!

Au revoir!
Au revoir!

Bonsoir, monsieur!
Bonsoir, les enfants!

Bonne nuit!

6 Écris les phrases dans les bulles.

Bonjour, mademoiselle!

Bonsoir, monsieur!

Bonne nuit, maman!

Bonjour, Thierry!

Bonjour, madame!

Bonjour, Lucile!

Bonsoir, Thierry!

Bonne nuit, Lucile!

7 Qu'est-ce qu'il y a dans ma trousse?

(Page 27)

Dans ma trousse, il y a ....

....

....

....

....

8 C'est - ce sont.

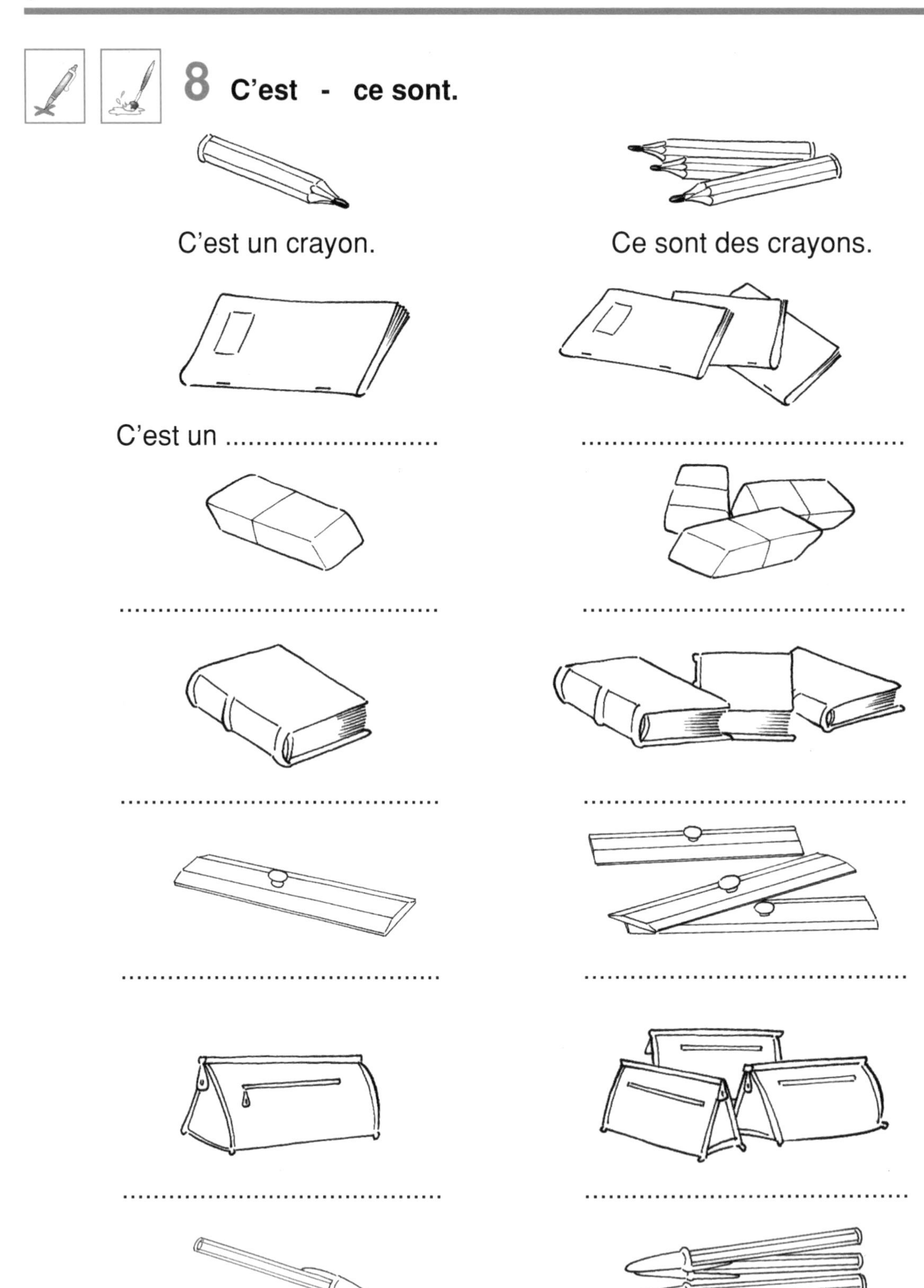

C'est un crayon. | Ce sont des crayons.

C'est un .... | ....

.... | ....

.... | ....

.... | ....

.... | ....

.... | ....

cahier - livre - gomme - règle - stylo - trousse

9 Qu'est-ce qu'ils ont?

Lucile a une gomme et des crayons. ....

....

....

....

Thierry - Salah - un cahier - un livre - une gomme
Gaston - des ciseaux - des stylos - un stick de colle

10 Voici un superbe arc-en-ciel! Colorie-le!

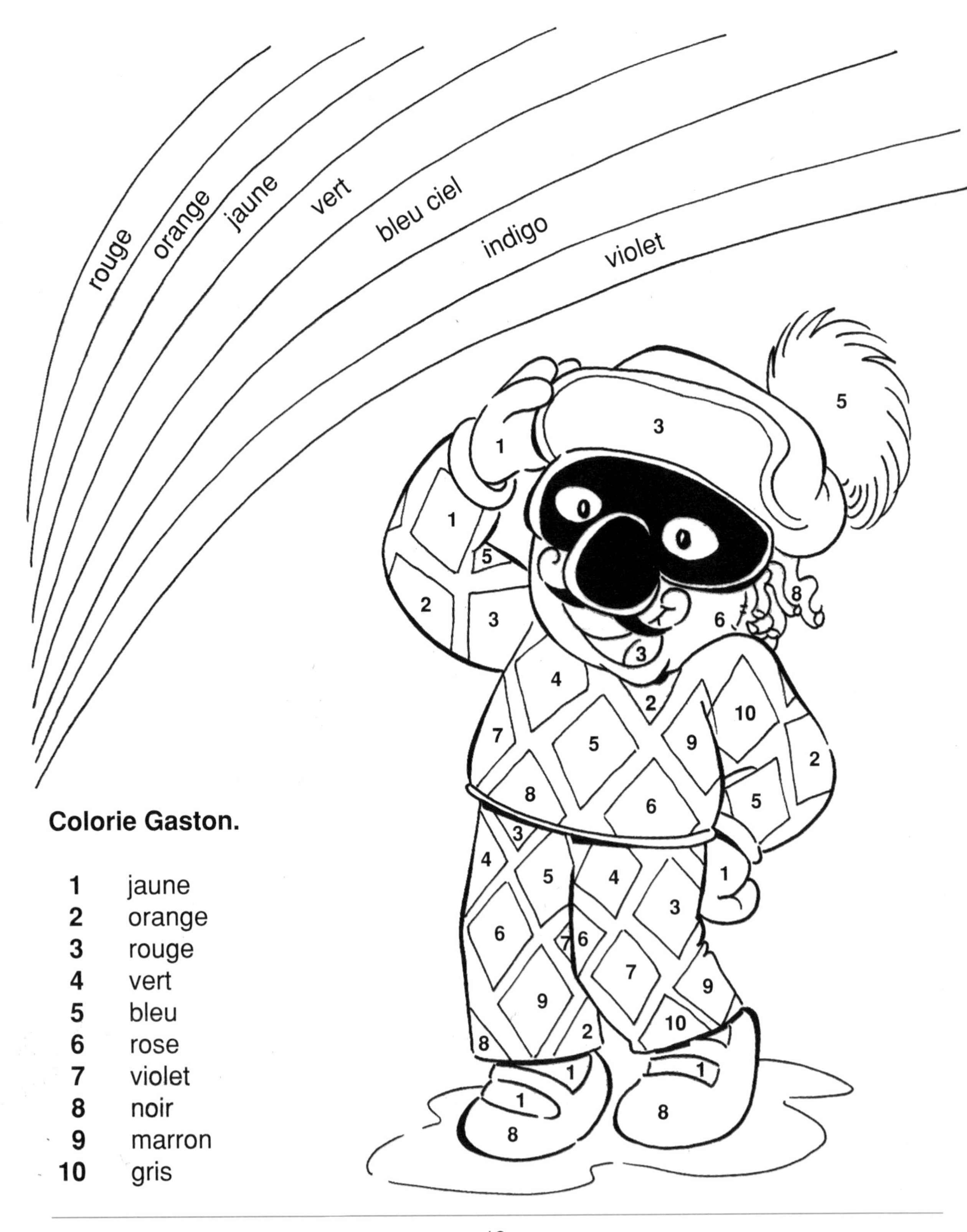

Colorie Gaston.

1	jaune
2	orange
3	rouge
4	vert
5	bleu
6	rose
7	violet
8	noir
9	marron
10	gris

11 De quelle couleur?

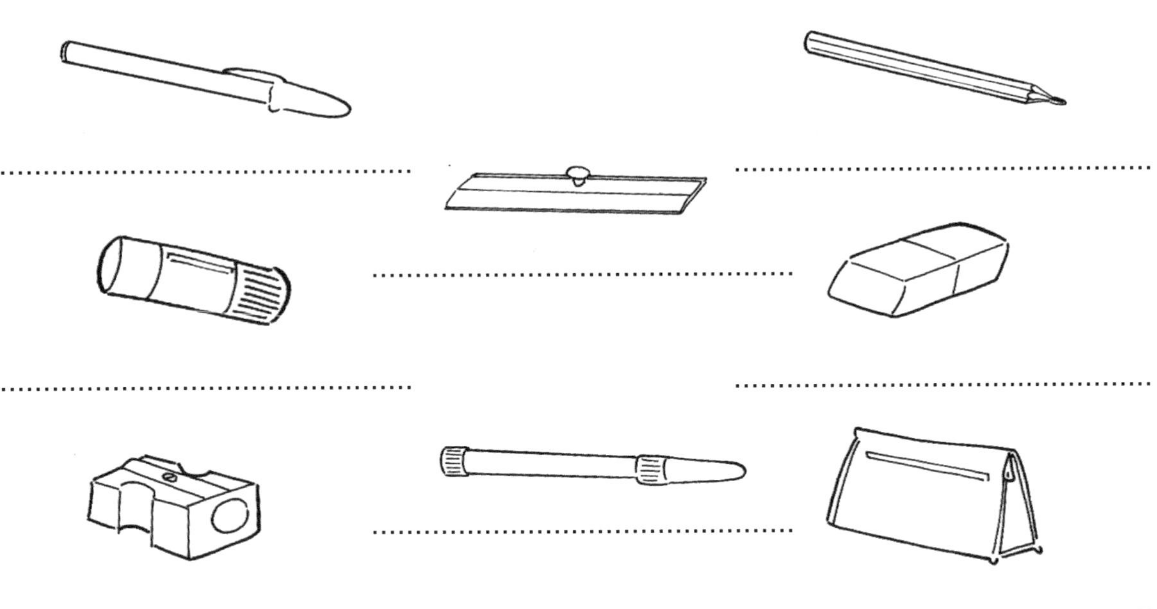

le stylo est vert - la gomme est verte - le crayon est blanc - la colle est blanche
le taille-crayon est gris - la règle est grise - le feutre est violet - la trousse est violette

12 Colorie selon les indications.

La porte est marron.

La balle est orange.

La gomme est rose et bleu.

Un feutre est jaune,
l'autre est vert.

Le cahier est vert.

Les livres sont rouges.

La chaise est bleue.

La table est rouge.

13 **Relie chaque nombre à son nom. Utilise plusieurs couleurs.**

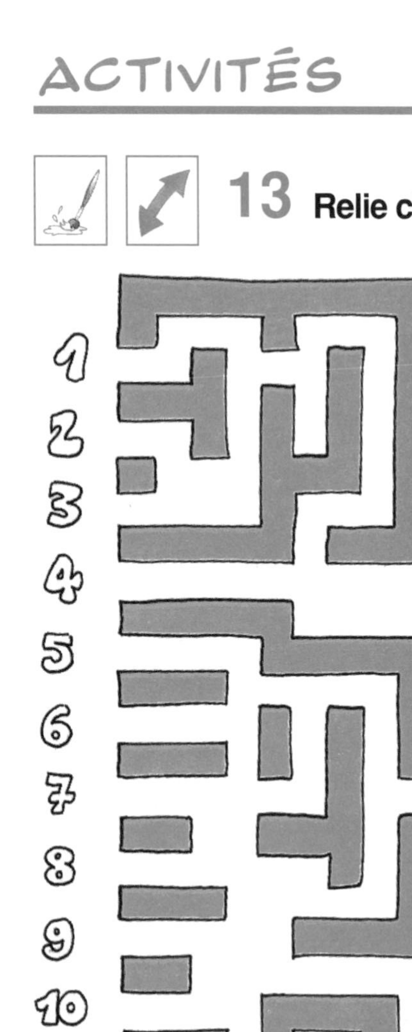

14 Pairs ou impairs?

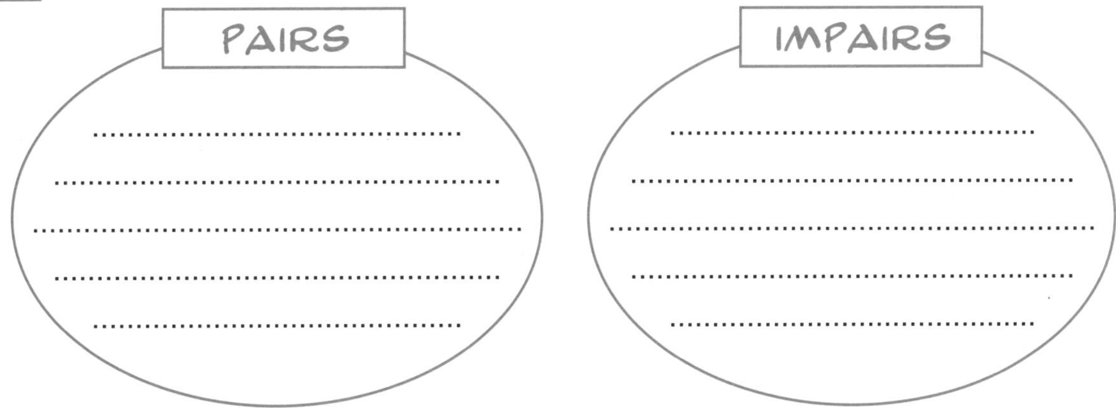

deux - six - dix-neuf - sept - neuf - dix - douze - trois - treize - seize - dix-sept
quatre - cinq - un - huit - dix-huit - quatorze - quinze - vingt - onze

15 L'aquarium arc-en-ciel.

Dans l'aquarium, il y a:
trois poissons rouges
deux poissons noirs
quatre poissons jaunes
un poisson violet
cinq poissons verts
six poissons orange
deux poissons roses

16 Vrai ou faux?

Sur la table, il y a:

	vrai	faux
trois oranges	❑	❑
deux cahiers	❑	❑
quatre stylos	❑	❑
six gommes	❑	❑
cinq bananes	❑	❑
dix champignons	❑	❑
trois livres	❑	❑
sept pommes	❑	❑

Retrouve les mots dans la grille.

C	H	A	M	P	I	G	N	O	N	S
B	K	C	W	X	G	O	M	M	E	S
A	S	A	N	B	C	X	G	B	X	K
N	V	H	J	L	I	V	R	E	S	X
A	Y	I	P	K	J	H	B	G	F	E
N	H	E	B	S	T	Y	L	O	S	W
E	T	R	Q	Z	W	I	L	K	J	Q
S	Z	S	U	L	P	O	M	M	E	S
O	R	A	N	G	E	S	U	J	W	X

17 Qu'est-ce que c'est?

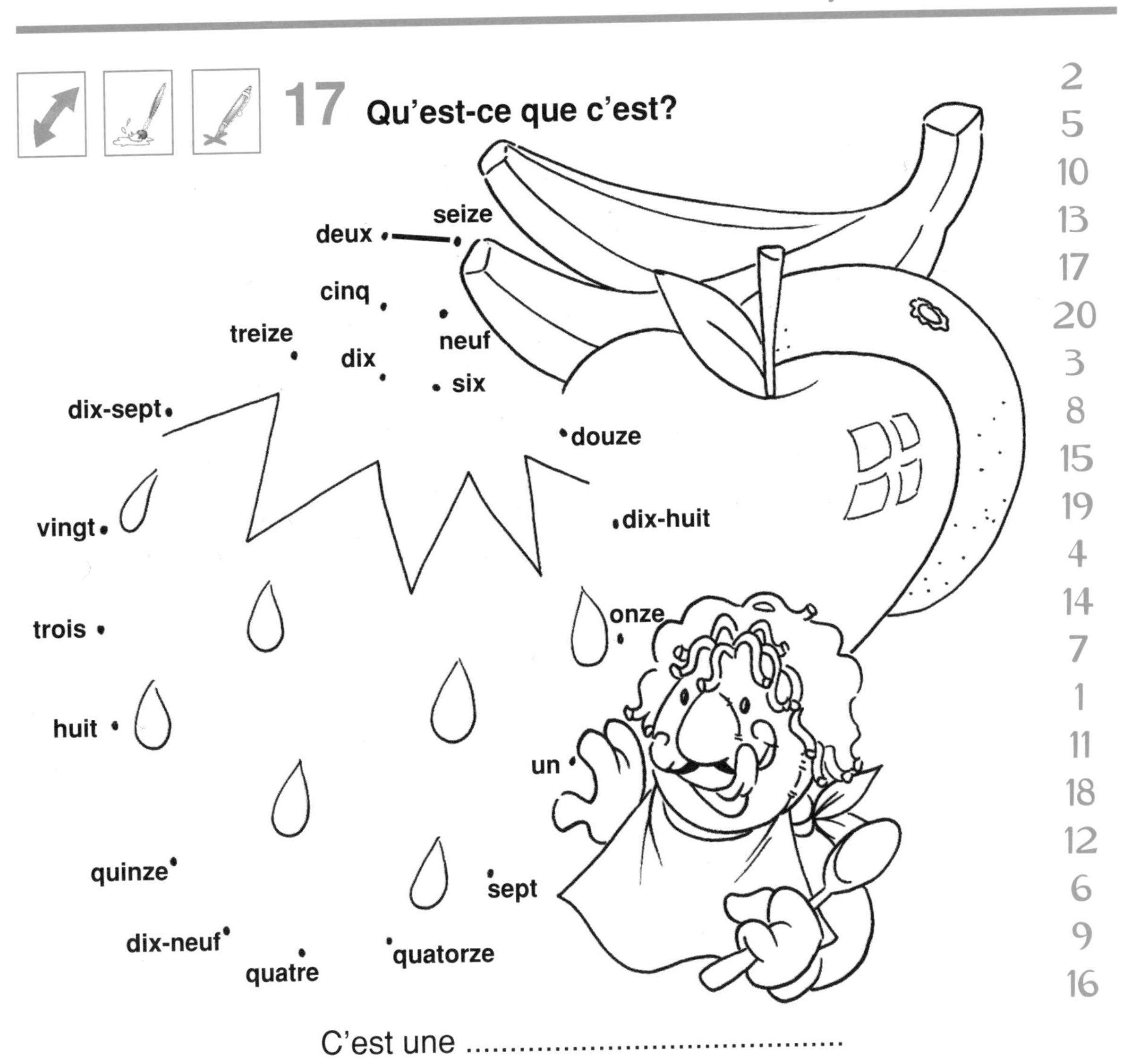

C'est une ....

18 Fais les soustractions, puis colorie selon les indications.

–	0	1	2	3	4	5	6
10	10	9	8				
11							
12							
13							
14							
15							
16							

11: jaune

12: orange

13: rouge

4 et 14: vert clair

5 et 15: vert foncé

6 et 16: bleu ciel

7: bleu marine

8: rose

9: violet

10: blanc

19 Qui est à l'appareil?

20 Construis ton téléphone!

21 Qu'est-ce que c'est?

(Page 29)

C'est ....

22 Quel âge as-tu?

(Page 27)

23 L'anniversaire de nos amis.

JANVIER

FÉVRIER

MARS

AVRIL

MAI

JUIN

JUILLET

OCTOBRE

DÉCEMBRE

Thierry est né en ....

Aline est née en ....

Pierre est né en ....

Lucile ....

Salah ....

24 Quelle heure est-il?

25 L'heure exacte. Dessine les aiguilles.

26 Le temps.

(Page 29)

  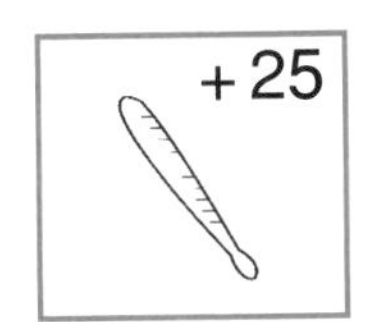

Il fait beau, il y a du soleil et il fait chaud.

Il fait mauvais, il pleut et il fait froid.

 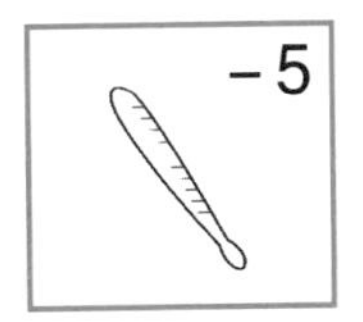

Il fait beau **mais** il fait froid.

27 Que font-ils? Écris le jour sous chaque image.

....

....

....

....

....

....

....

Lundi. Pierre va à l'école.
Mardi. Salah lit un livre.
Mercredi. Lucile va au parc.
Jeudi. Gaston mange un gâteau.
Vendredi. Salah regarde la télé.
Samedi. Lucile va au marché.
Dimanche. Thierry va au cinéma.

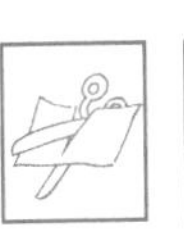

Page 9

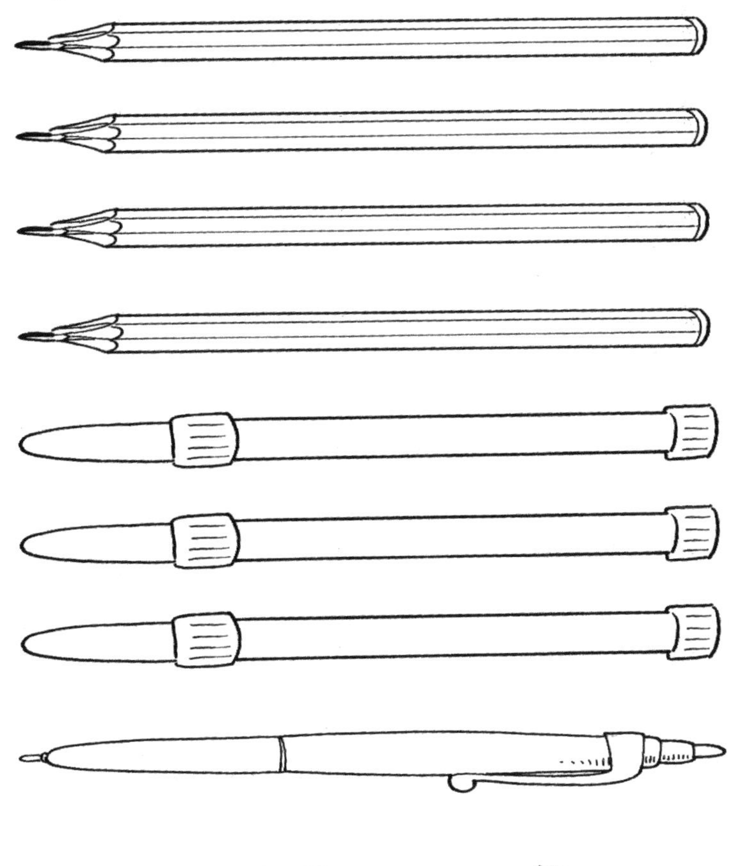

Page 22

Elle a trois ans.

Quel âge as-tu?

Quel âge a-t-il?

J'ai quatre ans.

Il a un an.

Quel âge a-t-elle?

Page 5

Bonne nuit!

Bonjour!

Bonsoir!

Page 6

Bonjour, les enfants!

Salut!

Bonjour, les enfants!

Bonjour, mademoiselle!

Au revoir, mademoiselle!

Au revoir, monsieur!

Bonjour, monsieur!

Bonjour, madame Lanot!

Bonsoir, mademoiselle!

Bonjour, monsieur Morel!

Bonsoir, monsieur!

Salut!

Page 21

Page 25

Il y a du soleil.	Il y a du vent.	Il y a des nuages.
Il neige.	Il pleut.	Il y a du brouillard.

28 Vive les vacances!

Les cahiers d'activités de Gaston proposent une foule d'exercices amusants qui complètent parfaitement les activités présentées dans les livres correspondants.
Utilisés à l'école ou à la maison, ils permettent à l'élève de consolider les connaissances qu'il a acquises au cours des leçons.

ISBN 88-8148-347-5

The Bow of the Wreck

A well preserved large anchor-winch is situated in the middle of the bow.

The wreck of the Thistlegorm

In an Upright Position

The intact bow of the wreck points to the North, the direction of navigation before the vessel sank. The port side anchor is still in its place whereas the starboard anchor lays 150 metres away from the hull.

The wreck of the Thistlegorm

HE GREAT SHIPWRECKS OF THE RED SEA

ALBERTO SILIOTTI

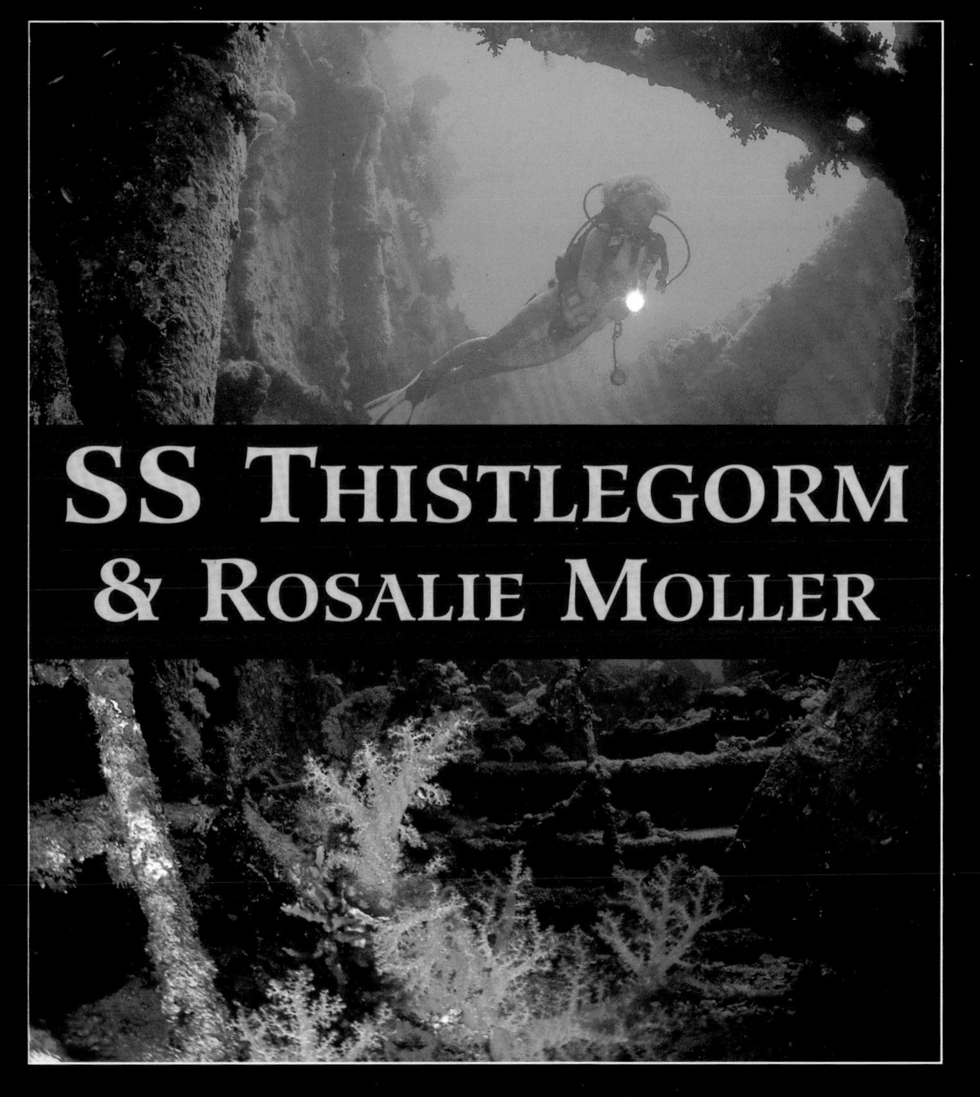

GEODIA EDIZIONI

OVER THE WRECK

Every day, dozens of diving boats tie up on the infrastructure of the *Thistlegorm* which often leads to considerable damage on the wreck.

Sha'ab Ali

Divers Explore the Wreck

Having descended down the rope, in this case tied at the bow, divers start exploring its structures.

The wreck of the Thistlegorm

Text Alberto Siliotti

Photographs Claudio Bertasini, Manfred Bortoli, Claudio Cangini, Fabio Casarotti, Francesco Chemell, Arnaud Chicurel, Federico Forletta, Alessandro Noro, Vincenzo Paolillo, Roberto Rinaldi, Alberto Siliotti, Stefano Zaffonato

Drawings Stefania Cossu, Giovanni Paulli, Stefano Trainito

Underwater Surveys Alessandro Banfo, Stefania Cossu, Claudio Di Manao, Federico Forletta, Alberto Siliotti, Stefano Trainito, Elena Zaffonato

General Editing Yvonne Marzoni Fecia di Cossato

English translation Sophie Schlöndorff and Felicity Lutz (*Scriptum*, Rome)

Printed in Egypt
ISBN 88-87177-69-4

On the photo: One of the stairways to the forecastle at the bow of the Thistlegorm *now torn away by a diving boat that tied up here*

Contents

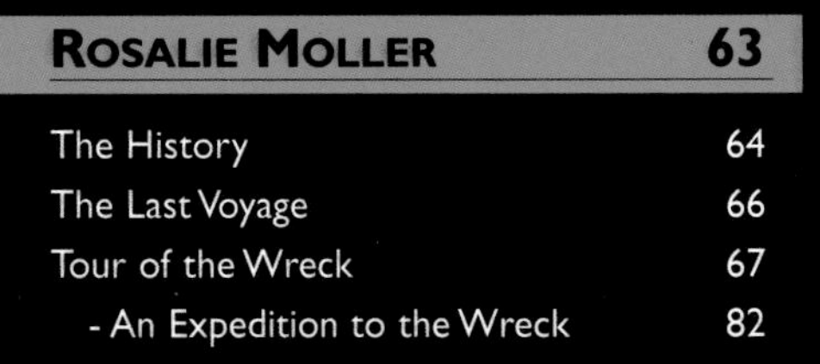

The Thistlegorm*'s stern*

The 40-millimeter anti-aircraft machine gun on the emplacement at the Thistlegorm*'s stern*

The bow of the Rosalie Moller

The Red Sea Shipwrecks

After the opening of the Suez Canal, the Carnatic *was one of the first victims in the Strait of Gubal*

Since antiquity, the Red Sea had been one of the main maritime routes along which merchandise from Africa and from the Middle and the Far East arrived in the Mediterranean basin, after being unloaded at Suez and transported from there, over land, to the Mediterranean coast. In more recent times, the opening of the Suez Canal, in 1869, created a direct sea link to the Mediterranean, vastly increasing the number of ships plying the Red Sea, whose waters held considerable dangers, especially in the northern area at the level of the Strait of Gubal, which are the southernmost end of the long Gulf of Suez. The many reefs and islands, the almost constant presence of northeasterly winds that were sometimes very strong, and the lack of adequate maps and efficient navigation systems all contributed to causing many shipwrecks, as can be seen from the impressive number of hulks still to be found in this stretch of sea. During World War II, the waters of the Red Sea became even more treacherous due to the presence of a German air base on the island of Crete, whose bombers had the task, among other things, of intercepting and sinking enemy convoys attempting to reach the Mediterranean. This is precisely what happened to the *Thistlegorm* and the *Rosalie Moller*, the two main wrecks in the northern Red Sea.

Satellite view of the Strait of Gubal

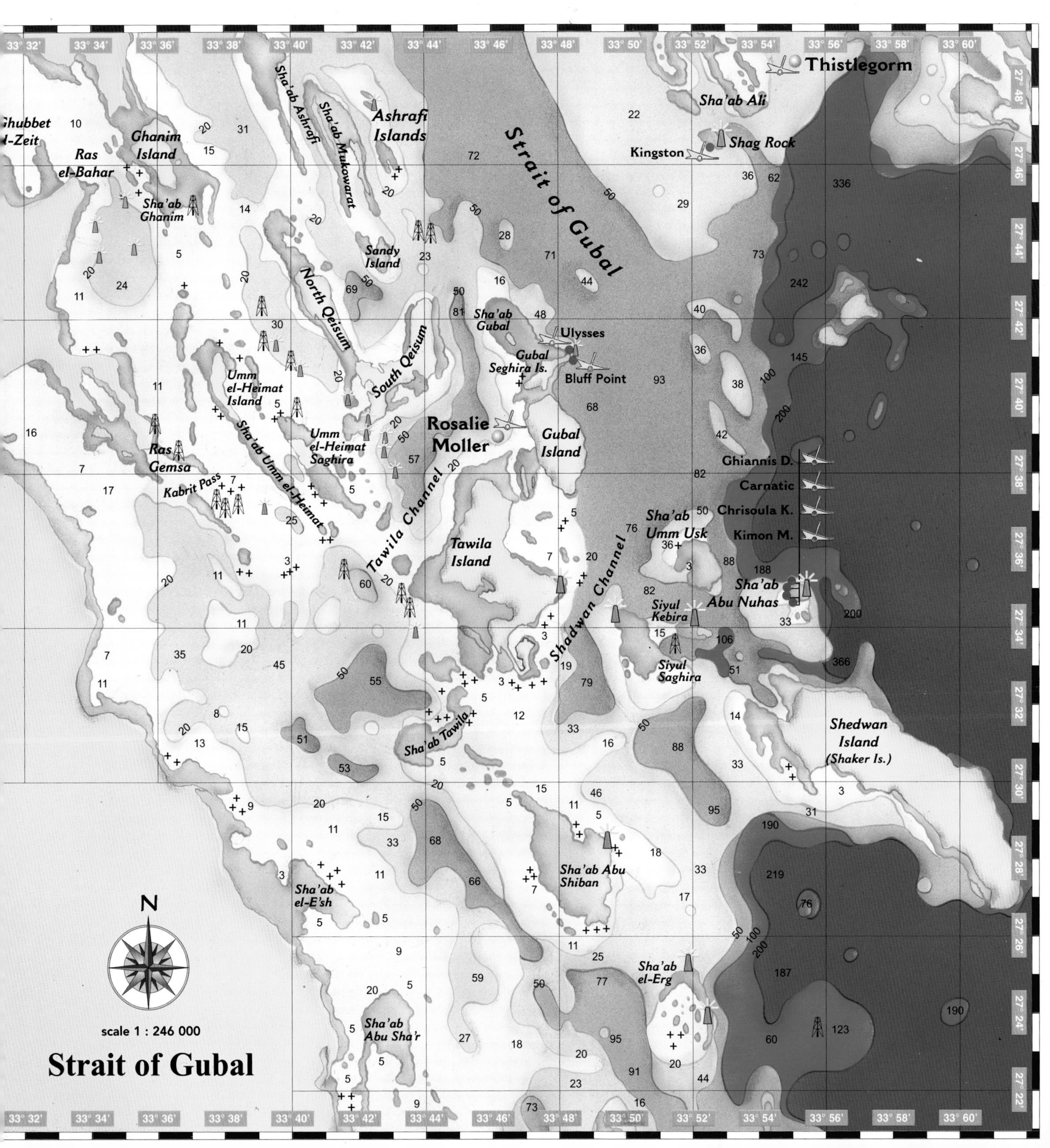

Strait of Gubal
scale 1 : 246 000
N
Thistlegorm
Sha'ab Ali
Shag Rock
Kingston
Ashrafi Islands
Sha'ab Ashrafi
Sha'ab Mukowarat
Ghanim Island
Ras el-Bahar
Sha'ab Ghanim
Sandy Island
North Qeisum
South Qeisum
Sha'ab Gubal
Ulysses
Gubal Seghira Is.
Bluff Point
Umm el-Heimat Island
Sha'ab Umm el-Heimat
Umm el-Heimat Saghira
Rosalie Moller
Gubal Island
Ras Gemsa
Kabrit Pass
Tawila Channel
Tawila Island
Shadwan Channel
Ghiannis D.
Carnatic
Chrisoula K.
Kimon M.
Sha'ab Umm Usk
Sha'ab Abu Nuhas
Siyul Kebira
Siyul Saghira
Sha'ab Tawila
Shedwan Island (Shaker Is.)
Sha'ab Abu Shiban
Sha'ab el-E'sh
Sha'ab el-Erg
Sha'ab Abu Sha'r

Exploring the Wreck

The corridor of the upper deck of the *Thistlegorm* is particularly awe-inspiring.

The wreck of the Thistlegorm

SS THISTLEGORM

The History

The Thistlebrae, *another* Albyn Line *ship, closely resembling the* Thistlegorm

The SS *Thistlegorm* (the initials SS in front of the name stand for "steam ship"), a British freighter belonging to the shipping company *Albyn Line Ltd*, was one of a group of vessels whose names began with the prefix "thistle," the national flower of Scotland and the shipping company's logo.

A total of eighteen ships in the *Thistle* series were launched and Gaelic words were added to the prefix indicating various types of thistle, such as the *Thistledhu* (*dhu* meaning "black"), the *Thistleroy* (*roy* meaning "red"), and the famous *Thistlegorm* (*gorm* meaning "blue").

The *Thistlegorm* weighed 4,898 tons (9,009 displacement tons), was 126.5 meters long, and had a three-cylinder, triple expansion steam engine capable of reaching an output of 1,850 horsepower, giving the ship a speed of approximately 10.5 knots. Launched on 9 April 1940 at the shipyard of *Thompson & Sons Ltd* in Sunderland, the *Thistlegorm* was a freighter assigned to transport supplies and war material to the British armed forces at the beginning of World War II. To protect it against possible

THE *THISTLEGORM'S* VOYAGES

The year after it was launched, the Thistlegorm *made three voyages: the first was to the United States, where it loaded airplanes and a supply of steel rails; the second brought it to Argentina where it embarked a shipment of grain; and the third took it to the Antilles to load rum and cane sugar.*

THE *ALBYN LINE* COMPANY

The Albyn Line Ltd *was founded on 21 June 1901 by William Allan as the* Thistle Ship Co. Ltd, *however, when he went to register it, he discovered that there was already a company by that name so he changed it to* Albyn Line, Albyn *(meaning "dawn") being the Gaelic name for Scotland.*

The funnels of all the Albyn Line *ships were decorated with a thistle, the company's logo.*

The Albyn Line *continued to be active through 29 March 1966, when it closed down after the sale of its last three ships, the* Thistledowne, *the* Thistledhu, *and the* Thistleroy.

The only existing photograph of the Thistlegorm *shows the ship being launched at Sunderland (UK) on 9 April 1940*

air attacks, it was fitted with light weaponry consisting in a 4.7-inch light anti-aircraft gun and a 40-millimeter anti-aircraft machine gun.

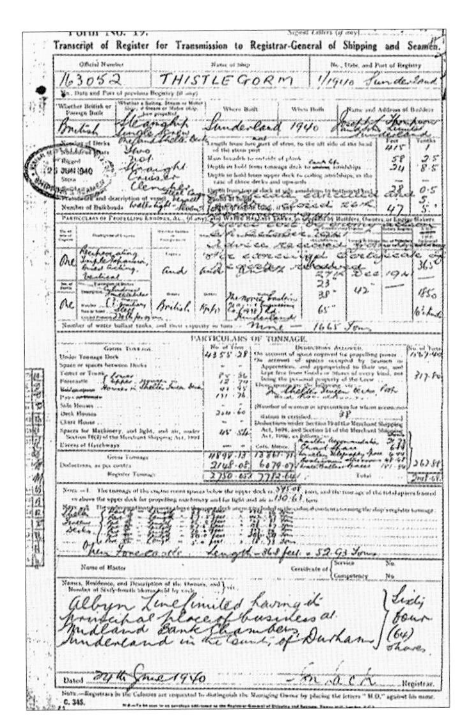
Form No. 19.

Transcript of Register for Transmission to Registrar-General of Shipping and Seamen.

Official Number	Name of Ship	No., Date, and Port of Registry
163052	THISTLEGORM	1/1940 Sunderland

Whether British or Foreign Built	Where Built	When Built
British	Sunderland	1940

Length from fore part of stem, to the aft side of the head of the stern post: 415 · 1
Main breadth to outside of plank: 58 · 2.5
Depth in hold from tonnage deck to ceiling amidships: 24 · 8.5
Number of Bulkheads: 47 · 5

Number of water ballast tanks, and their capacity in tons: None — 1665 Tons

PARTICULARS OF TONNAGE

Open Forecastle Length – 36.8 feet = 52.93 Tons

Name of Master — Certificate of Service No. / Competency No.

Names, Residence, and Description of the Owners, and Number of Sixty-fourth Shares held by each, viz.:
Albyn Line Limited having its principal place of business at Midland Bank Chambers, Sunderland in the County of Durham — Sixty four (64) shares

Dated 24th June 1940 — Registrar.

Note.—Registrars in the Colonies are requested to distinguish the Managing Owner by placing the letters "M.O." against his name.

C. 345.

The Thistlegorm's *specifications, entered in the British Shipping Register*

The Thistledhu, *another ship similar to the* Thistlegorm, *was sold by the* Albyn Line *in 1965*

Operation Crusader

The *Thistlegorm* took part in the secret mission code-named *Operation Crusader*, intended to deliver supplies to the 200,000-strong British 8th Army stationed in Egypt and Cyrenaica (Eastern Libya) under the command of Field Marshal Bernard Montgomery. Libya had already been occupied by Italy in 1912 and, at the beginning of World War II, it had become an important base for the troops of the Axis, as the Italian-German alliance was called.
The coalition soldiers had the task of pushing eastward from Libya to conquer Alexandria and Suez. In September 1940, the Italian 10th Army had advanced considerably, provoking the first British offense between 9 December 1940 and 7 February 1941. On 31 March, however, the Italian-German counteroffensive took place, and the Axis troops, under the command of Field Marshal Erwin Rommel, routed the British forces and reoccupied the whole of Cyrenaica. Subsequently, the British, under the command of Sir Claude John Auchinleck, decided to launch a second offensive, scheduled for November 1941, however, they urgently needed new supplies to carry out this action. The Axis troops stationed in Libya controlled the entire eastern Mediterranean, while Egypt remained solidly in the hands of the British. Consequently, the safest way to deliver war material and other supplies required by the British troops to the port of Alexandria was to circumnavigate Africa, round the Cape of Good Hope, sail back up through the Red Sea, and finally through the Suez Canal. Despite the fact that this route was much longer than the direct one across the Mediterranean, it permitted British convoys to reach the port of Alexandria in relative safety. To this end, Auchinleck planned *Operation Crusader*: a convoy of no less than 16 vessels, including the *Thistlegorm*, was to circumnavigate Africa to ensure that his troops received the necessary supplies for the new offensive. However, the German air force under the command of General Hans Seidemann had deployed a squadron (*Geschwader*) of roughly 90 airplanes to Crete, in order to control navigation in the Suez Canal and along the Red Sea routes. The *Thistlegorm* and the *Rosalie Moller* were to become two of its victims...

Field Marshal Erwin Rommel, commander of the Axis troops, in northern Africa

Field Marshal Bernard Montgomery, commander of the British 8th Army

Kampfgeschwader KG 26's *coat of arms*

The Last Voyage

In May 1941, the *Thistlegorm*, with a crew of 39 men under the command of Captain William Ellis, left the port of Glasgow in Scotland and headed toward Alexandria. This was to be her last voyage.

The ship was carrying ammunitions of different kind, antitank mines; *Lee Enfield MK III* rifles; some one hundred *BSA W-M20*, *Matchless G3L*, and *Norton 16 H* motorcycles; *Bedford*, *Morris*, and *Ford* trucks; transport trailers; portable field generators; spare parts for airplanes and land vehicles; medicines; tires; and rubber boots. Two *Universal Carrier MK II* light tanks and two *Stanier 8 F* steam engines, with coal tenders and water tank wagons, essential for crossing desert areas, completed the cargo.

After a brief stop at Cape Town in South Africa (where she replenished her fuel, water, and food supplies) and at Aden in Southern Yemen, the *Thistlegorm*, one of a convoy of 16 ships and escorted by the cruiser HMS *Carlisle*, was sailing back up through the Red Sea when she received the order to cast anchor in the Strait of Gubal and wait her turn to pass through the Suez Canal, which had been temporarily obstructed by a ship that had struck a German mine.

William Ellis, captain of the Thistlegorm

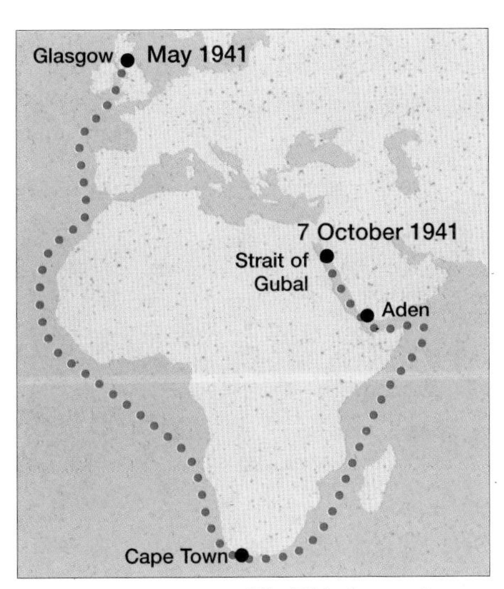

The Thistlegorm*'s route*

The *Thistlegorm* therefore anchored in the lee of the great reef of *Sha'ab Ali*, which was considered a safe berth and code-named *Safe Anchorage F*. During the night between 5 and 6 October 1941, two German *Heinkel He 111* bombers belonging to the *Kampfgeschwader KG 26* stationed on the island of Crete happened to sight the ship by pure chance, while returning from an unsuccessful search for the *Queen Mary*, which was carrying Australian troops along the same route. They attacked

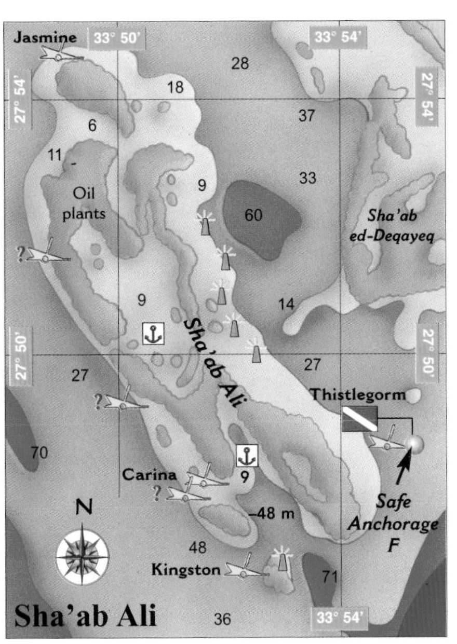

Safe Anchorage F *at Sha'ab Ali*

A BSA W-M20 *motorcycle issued to the British troops in northern Africa*

THE *HEINKEL HE* 111 PLANES

The Heinkel He 111, *named after its Inventor Ernst Heinkel, was the most common heavy bomber used by German aviation during World War II.*
Launched in 1934 as a fast transport plane, a total of 7,300 planes were built in various models. They had two propeller engines of 1,350 horsepower each, and a wingspan of 22.6 meters.
The Heinkel He 111 *could fly at a speed of over 400 kilometers per hour, arriving at a service ceiling of 8,500 meters, and it had an operating range of 2,060 kilometers.*
These airplanes that had a crew of five were armed with 6 machine guns and could carry 4 tons of bombs.

The Heinkel He 111 *was chosen to launch the first* V-1 *air/land missiles used to bomb England.*

SPECIFICATIONS
Wingspan *22.6 m*
Length *16.4 m*
Weight at take-off *14 tons*
Engine *2* Junkers Jumo 211 *with 12 cylinders*
Output *2x1,350 hp*
Maximum speed *405 km/h*
Ceiling *8,500 m*
Range *2,060 km*

Heinkel He 111 *bombers ready for take-off*

her at 0:35 am on 6 October. The attack came as a complete surprise, and the *Thistlegorm* had no time to defend herself. She was hit by two powerful bombs (containing two tons of explosive each) at the level of hold no. 4, near the engine room, and where the ammunition was stored. The explosion was all the more violent because the bombs also blew up the ship's boiler and most of the ammunition on board. The two locomotives, which had been placed on deck near hold no. 4, were catapulted into the air, despite their weight of a good 126 tons each, and sank approximately 30 meters from the hull, where they lie to this day.
At 1:30 am, the *Thistlegorm*, having split in two, sank rapidly, coming to rest upright and on an even keel on the flat, sandy seabed at a depth of a little over 30 meters.
The captain and his crew were saved by the HMS *Carlisle*, which happened to be in the *Thistlegorm*'s immediate vicinity, but nine men,

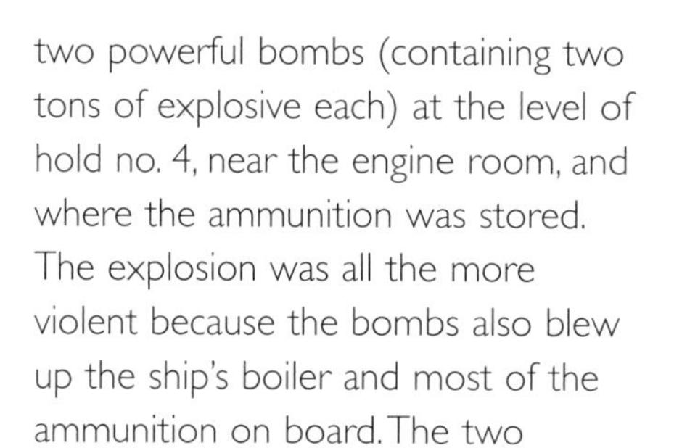
The cockpit of a Heinkel He 111

The cruiser HMS Carlisle

four sailors and five gunners, the youngest of whom was only seventeen, perished in the attack. When the *Thistlegorm* was discovered by divers and became the subject of articles, books, and documentaries, some members of the crew played an active role in reconstructing the events. They included Glyn Owen, a *Royal Navy* gunner, who took part in the making of the *BBC* documentary *The Last Voyage of the Thistlegorm*; Henry Bansall, chief engineer; Ray Gibson, third radiotelegraph operator; Dennis Gray and John Whitman, who all contributed their memories and personal accounts to bring the story of the *Thistlegorm* back to life.

A Heinkel He 111 *bomber belonging to the* Kampfgeschwader KG 26 *squadron*

This photograph published in the Daily Mirror *shows several members of the* Thistlegorm*'s crew: the person standing on the right is the boatswain Mr. Graham; the arrow points to Angus MacLeay*

THE HERO OF THE *THISTLEGORM*

The sailor Angus MacLeay, asleep in his bunk, was awoken with a start when the attack occurred. With no time to get dressed, he rushed up on deck. The ship's deck was already ablaze, and MacLeay thought the only way to survive was to jump into the sea.
He remembered the events of that night in an article published in the Stornoway Gazette *in July 1942:*
"... I was about to jump into the sea, when I turned round and noticed a gunner lying on the deck, unconscious and surrounded by flames. I went toward him, but the deck was covered with pieces of glass that got stuck in my feet, and I had to stop and take them out before I could pick him up. After lifting him onto my shoulders, I tried to reach the lifeboats through the flames..."
MacLeay thus managed to save his companion's life, getting off with only two weeks in hospital.
For his heroism, he was awarded the George Medal *by King George VI. Subsequently, Angus MacLeay returned to his home in the Hebrides, near Stornoway, where he died in 1991.*

The Discovery of the Wreck

The first dive to the Thistlegorm *was made by Albert Falco and Frédéric Dumas in March 1955, on the way to the Indian Ocean on board the* Calypso

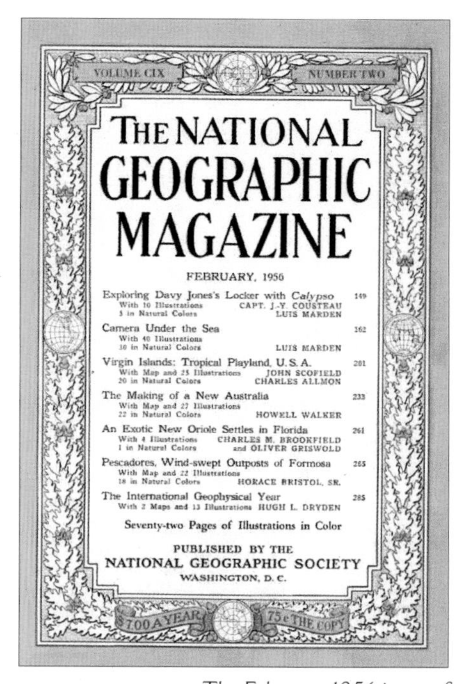

VOLUME CIX NUMBER TWO

THE NATIONAL GEOGRAPHIC MAGAZINE

FEBRUARY, 1956

Seventy-two Pages of Illustrations in Color

PUBLISHED BY THE NATIONAL GEOGRAPHIC SOCIETY
WASHINGTON, D. C.

$7.00 A YEAR 75¢ THE COPY

The February 1956 issue of National Geographic, *featuring the first article about the* Thistlegorm

Captain Jacques-Yves Cousteau discovered the wreck of the *Thistlegorm* in March 1955, while on his way to the Indian Ocean on board his famous research ship, the *Calypso*, to carry out a long scientific mission that was to take him over 15,000 miles, all the way to Madagascar.

The two leading members of Cousteau's crew, Albert Falco and Frédéric Dumas, dove down to the wreck several times, together with cameraman Philippe Agostini, and documented their discovery using one of the first underwater movie cameras. These momentous scenes were included in the famous documentary that Cousteau produced and co-directed with Louis Malle, *Le monde du silence* (1955).

The first photographs of the wreck were published in a long article that appeared in *National Geographic* magazine in February 1956.

The vessel with its cargo that Cousteau found was virtually intact despite the explosion. It was possible to identify the wreck thanks to the discovery of the ship's bell, which was inscribed with its name.

Albert Falco and captain Jacques-Yves Cousteau

ALBERT FALCO

Albert Falco, head scuba diver and later captain of the famous Calypso, is the last surviving member of the 1955 expedition to the Red Sea and Indian Ocean, during which the Thistlegorm *was discovered.*
Falco was also the first man to live in the marine depths. In 1962, he and Claude Wesly, lived in a specially designed structure under water for eight days. His home is now in Marseille, and he is actively involved in various activities concerning marine conservation.

The ship's bell, inscribed with her name. This valuable object was stolen several years after the discovery of the wreck and its exact whereabouts are unknown

THE FIRST DIVE, 17 MARCH 1955

At the first light of dawn, the Calypso *began advancing, zigzagging along at reduced speed, until, after two hours, thanks to our fathometer, our efforts were crowned with success. Half an hour later, I had the great honor of accompanying my head scuba diver* [Dumas] *on the first dive to the wreck.*
The alignment of its two masts guided us toward the unknown. Behind us, dozens of small fish accompanied us out of curiosity.
A few kicks of our flippers brought us to the imposing forecastle; here, a young sea turtle resting on the capstan suddenly rose up, inviting us to swim over the keel and heavy chain hanging from the starboard hawsehole, where a magnificent blue angel fish with yellow patches was hiding. We observed the bronze bell, on which Dumas later made out the ship's name by using a knife to prize away an oyster and a group of soft corals that had chosen to live there. Near the first hold, we saw railway wagons completely covered with oysters and flaming Alcyonacea.
We slipped inside, swimming from one surprise to another, and in the depths of the freighter we found an incredible shipment of war material: dozens of BSA *and* Norton *motorcycles, neatly loaded onto trucks alongside* [Morris Commercial] *jeeps, and crates of ammunition. Further along, we made out the tracks of small tanks, many tires, and large caliber howitzers, as well as soldiers' uniforms and boots. Ascending in front of the walkway of the bridge, we could see the compass and the radiogoniometer's double-handled movable antenna, in good condition. As we approached, a dozen or so thick-lipped groupers escaped through the torn sheet metal. An enormous shoal of lutianid hunted in the blue above us.*
All this chaos made me think that the impact of a torpedo or bomb might have caused the explosion of the ammunition on board, and this freighter's tragic end. During the dive, as we inspected the stern of the wreck, where an anti-aircraft gun is aimed eternally at the seabed, we encountered the most enormous Napoleonfish of all – in half a century of diving in waters around the world, I have never seen one quite so large. We estimated that it must have been at least one-and-a-half meters tall and three meters long!
But the Calypso *had to continue on its course toward the Indian Ocean to shoot 3/4 of the footage for the film* Le monde du silence *in three months. It returned to anchor by the* Thistlegorm *the 12, 13, and 14 June 1955.*
On this occasion, the entire crew dove down three times a day to shoot the images that would make up one of the most beautiful sequences in this first major underwater film, which won the Palme d'Or *in Cannes in 1956, and which was shown throughout the world …*
Personally, I was lucky enough to dive the wreck once again 41 years later … With the same excitement, camera in hand, I retraced my steps from keel to stern. It saddened me to see the devastating effects human beings have had on this fantastic marine monument.
Unfortunately, on the exterior, the masts have collapsed, the upper platform has caved in, and all the navigational instruments have disappeared. There are no longer any oysters, and the Alcyonacea have been greatly reduced, though the fish are still numerous. Fish and corals joined in osmosis have always reproduced to ensure the beauty, equilibrium, and conservation of the marine world, a sanctuary that profoundly stirs the imagination. Adopted by its fauna and flora, the Thistlegorm *has become part of this world. It is now up to us scuba divers to protect it for future generations…*

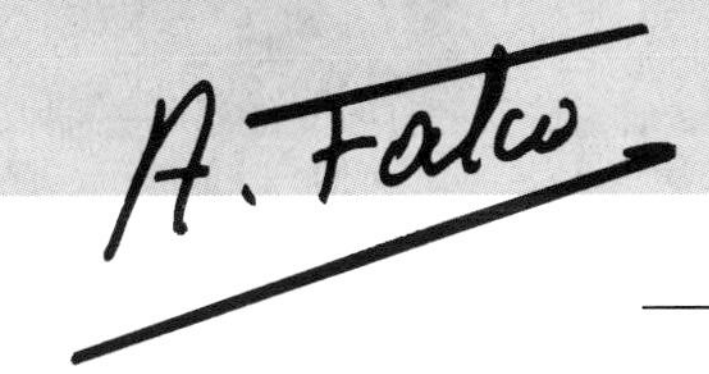

The Rediscovery

The *Thistlegorm* subsequently passed into obscurity for almost twenty years, until it was rediscovered in 1974 by the Israeli scuba diver Shimshon Machiah, who was taken to the site by a Bedouin fisherman from El-Tur. News of the rediscovery was kept secret, and the wreck remained known to only a closed circle of local divers over the following years.
In May 1992, a local skipper from Hurghada, Roger Winter, started taking the first tourists to visit the wreck, and in November the same year the *Thistlegorm* gained became famous due to an article written by two well-known divers, Alessandro Carletti and Settimio Cipriani published in the Italian journal *Aqua* which was followed by an article by John Bantin in the English *Diver* magazine. In 1994, Caroline Hawkins produced *Last Voyage of the Thistlegorm* for the *BBC*, the first documentary on this extraordinary wreck, which brought it to the attention of the general public. Considered the finest and most interesting of the Red Sea shipwrecks, a veritable "underwater museum of World War II," the *Thistlegorm* soon became a very popular attraction for divers from around the world.

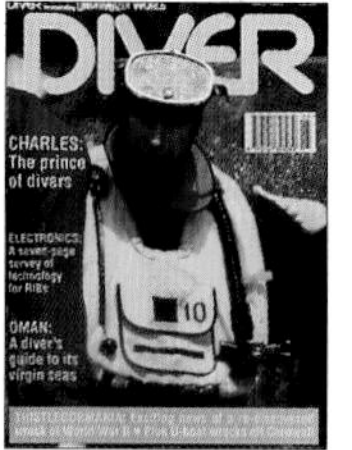

Brief History of the *Thistlegorm*

1940	... the *Thistlegorm* is launched in Sunderland (England).
1941 6 October	... two German *Heinkel He 111* bombers from Crete sink the *Thistlegorm* lying at anchor in the lee of the *Sha'ab Ali* reef.
1955	... Captain Cousteau and his crew discover the wreck of the *Thistlegorm*.
1956	... an article appears in the February issue of the American magazine *National Geographic*.
1957	... the wreck is forgotten ...
1974	... the *Thistlegorm* is rediscovered.
1992	... the *Thistlegorm* is officially rediscovered by recreational divers. The Italian magazine *Aqua* publishes the first article about the wreck.
1993	... the English magazine *Diver* publishes an article about the *Thistlegorm*.
1994	... the *BBC* produces the first important documentary on the wreck.

Equipped with a flashlight, a scuba diver enters the Thistlegorm*'s holds*

Tour of the Wreck

Divers on their safety stop holding on to the rope before re-entering the boat so as not to be carried away by the current that is often strong here

The *Thistlegorm* is located 38 miles from the port of Hurghada, and 31 miles from those of El-Gouna and Sharm el-Sheikh. An exploration of the wreck is usually carried out in two stages, after the boat has been moored to the external structure of the wreck at its stern or bow, a delicate operation performed by the guide. The first dive takes place in the morning, and is a general tour of the *Thistlegorm* resting in its NW-SE position. Unfortunately, visibility rarely exceeds 20–30 meters and there is frequently a tidal current that is sometimes quite strong flowing aft from the bow. It is thus necessary to submerge and resurface by holding on to one of the cables attaching the boat to the wreck. Over the years, a number of incompetent or irresponsible guides have caused significant damage by fastening the cables of their boats to fragile, or even unstable, parts of the wreck such as the stairways, loading derricks, handrail, and so on, instead of to solid structures capable of withstanding strong traction, such as the bollards, capstans, or propeller axle.

The wreck is reached by holding on to a cable

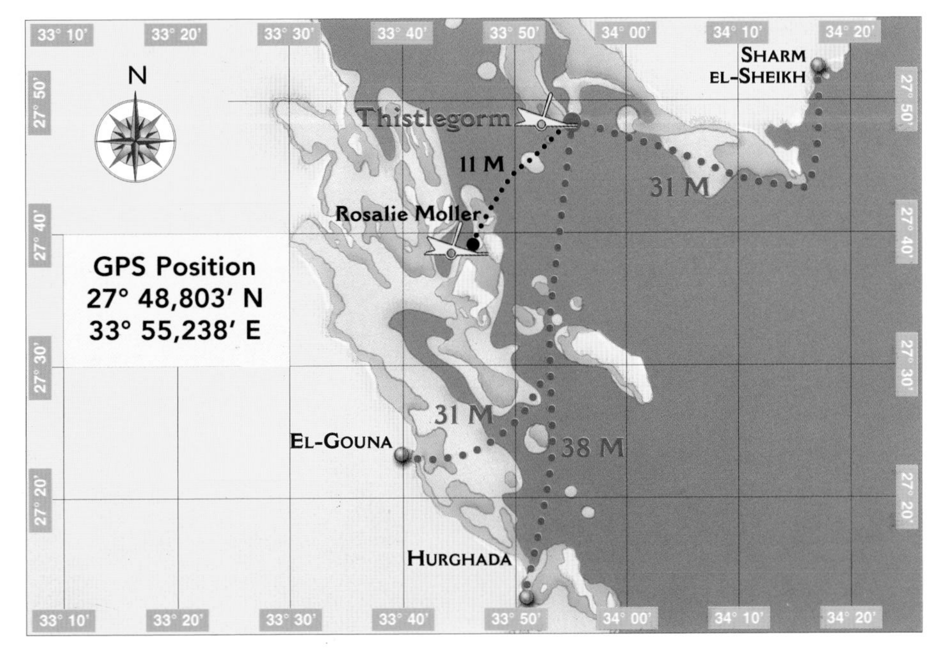

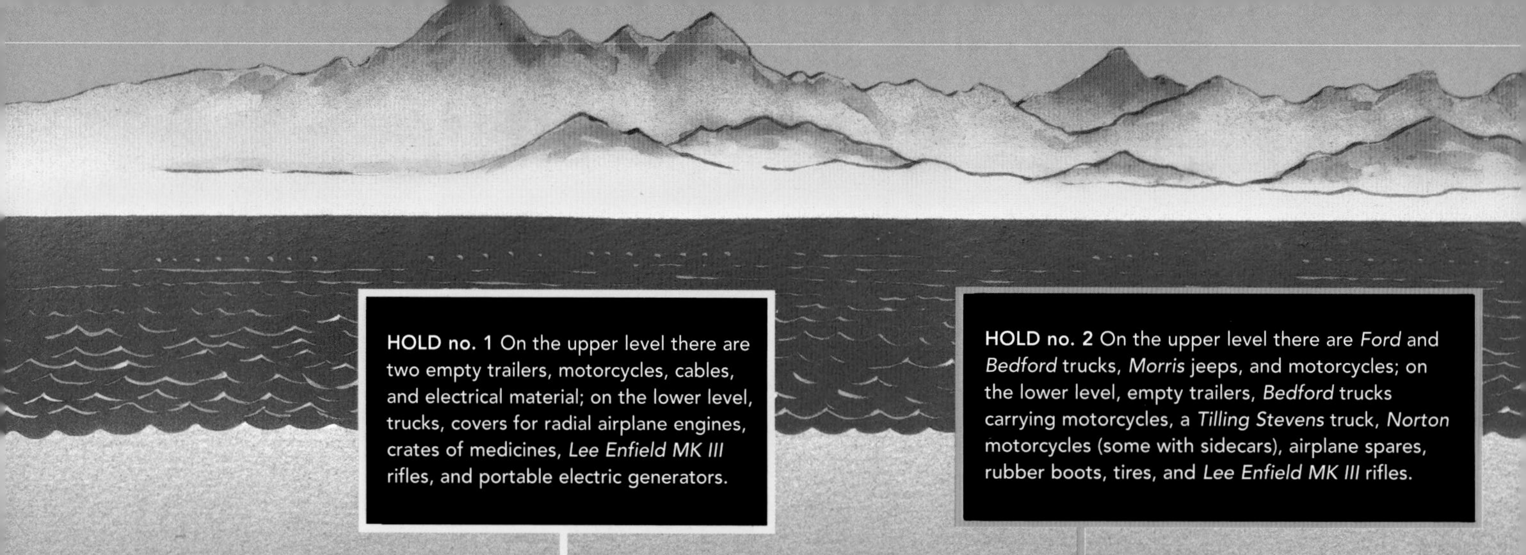

HOLD no. 1 On the upper level there are two empty trailers, motorcycles, cables, and electrical material; on the lower level, trucks, covers for radial airplane engines, crates of medicines, *Lee Enfield MK III* rifles, and portable electric generators.

HOLD no. 2 On the upper level there are *Ford* and *Bedford* trucks, *Morris* jeeps, and motorcycles; on the lower level, empty trailers, *Bedford* trucks carrying motorcycles, a *Tilling Stevens* truck, *Norton* motorcycles (some with sidecars), airplane spares, rubber boots, tires, and *Lee Enfield MK III* rifles.

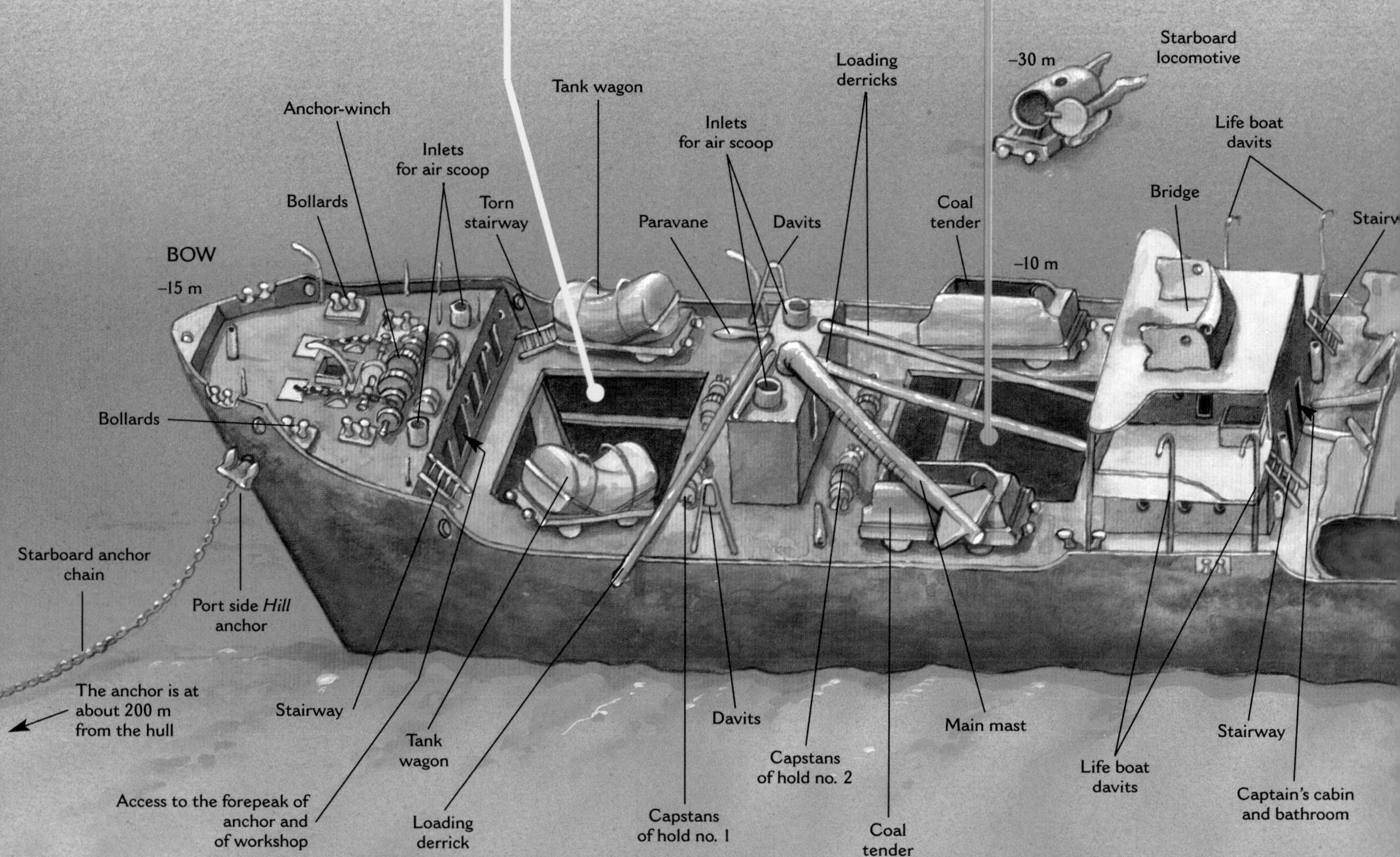

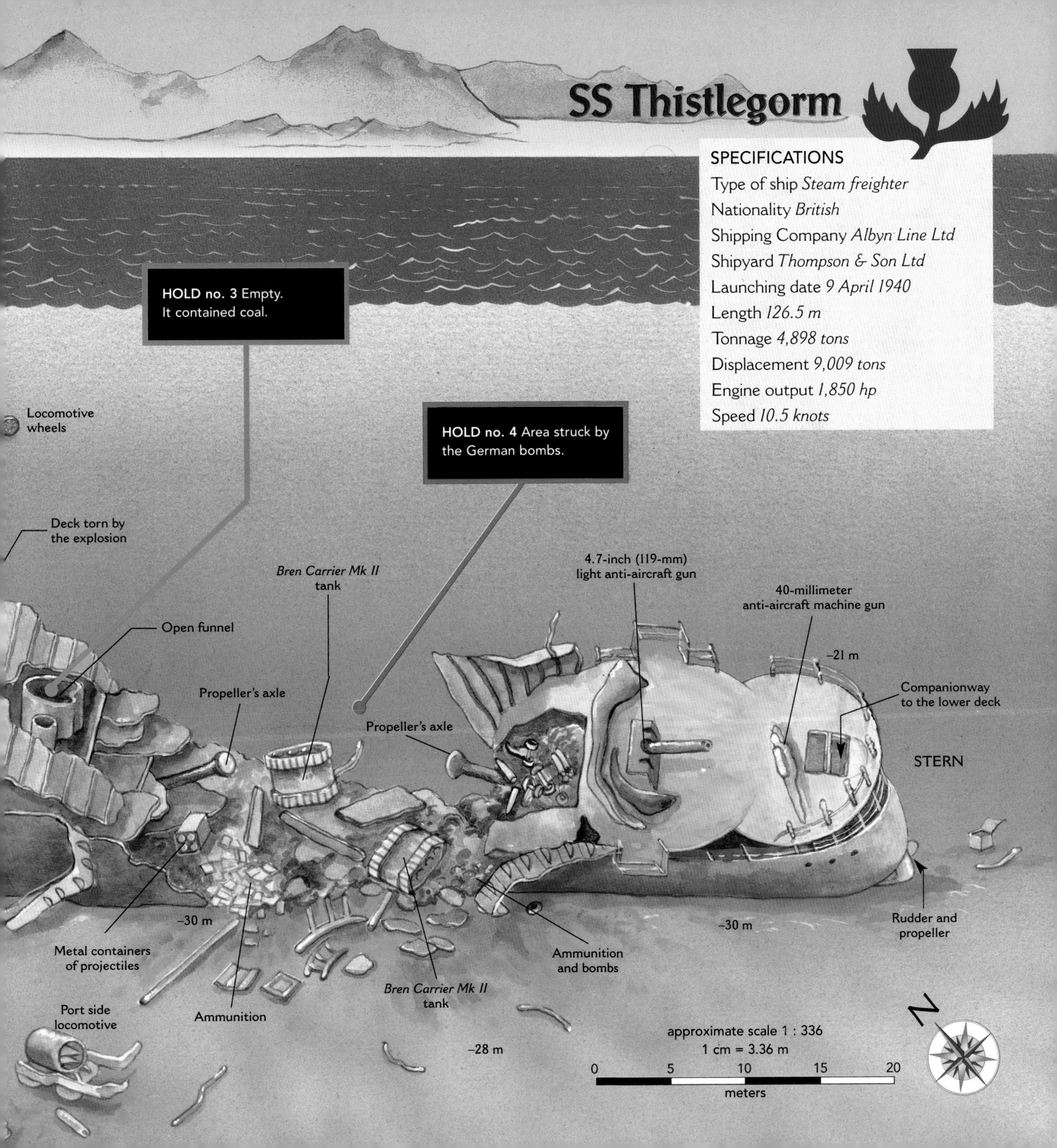

SS Thistlegorm
SPECIFICATIONS
Type of ship *Steam freighter*
Nationality *British*
Shipping Company *Albyn Line Ltd*
Shipyard *Thompson & Son Ltd*
Launching date *9 April 1940*
Length *126.5 m*
Tonnage *4,898 tons*
Displacement *9,009 tons*
Engine output *1,850 hp*
Speed *10.5 knots*
HOLD no. 3 Empty. It contained coal.
HOLD no. 4 Area struck by the German bombs.
Locomotive wheels
Deck torn by the explosion
Bren Carrier Mk II tank
4.7-inch (119-mm) light anti-aircraft gun
40-millimeter anti-aircraft machine gun
–21 m
Open funnel
Propeller's axle
Companionway to the lower deck
Propeller's axle
STERN
–30 m
–30 m
Rudder and propeller
Metal containers of projectiles
Ammunition and bombs
Bren Carrier Mk II tank
Port side locomotive
Ammunition
–28 m
approximate scale 1 : 336
1 cm = 3.36 m
0
5
10
15
20
meters
N

Survey of the Wreck

The stern with the four-bladed propeller and rudder

The stern lists to port at a 46° angle and, at its deepest point, at a depth of 30 meters, the four-bladed propeller and the rudder can be seen. Ascending several meters to a depth of –25, on the upper deck there is a 40-millimeter anti-aircraft machine gun and, a little further toward the bow, a light gun with a 4.7-inch (119-millimeter) gauge; dense shoals of glassfish or Red Sea dwarf sweeper (*Parapriacanthus ransonneti*) swim around between them.
Next there is the large gash caused by German bombs at the level of hold no. 4, which contained ammunition, bombs, two *Bren Carrier MK II* tanks (which now lie at the bottom, overturned but in good condition), and trailers to transport the ammunition. The ammunition, which, inexplicably, survived intact and can still be seen in situ, consists of 370-millimeter projectiles, originally packed in metal containers holding four each, and several large *MK 12* deep-sea mines, which contained approximately 400 kilograms of explosive each. Also clearly visible jutting through the gash are the two stumps of the propeller's axle.
Roughly 30 meters south-west of the hull from hold no. 4, at a depth of 28 meters, lies the first of two *Stanier 8 F* locomotives, which were part of the *Thistlegorm*'s cargo.
The main axis of the locomotive, of

A scuba diver exploring the Thistlegorm*'s front side*

The 40-millimeter anti-aircraft machine gun positioned on the emplacement at the Thistlegorm's *sterr*

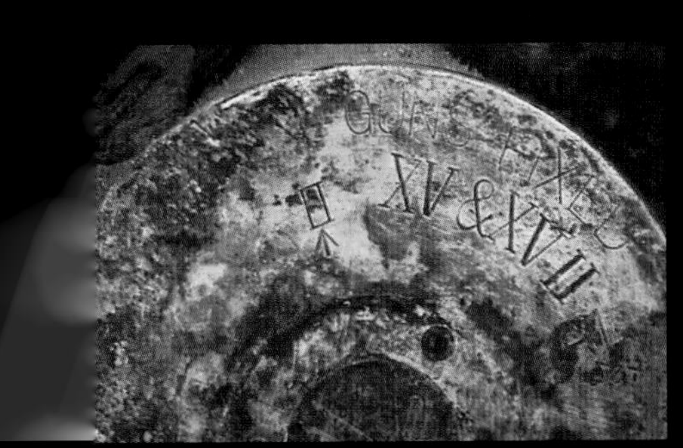

The base of a 370-millimeter projectile; he year of manufacture, 1935, is inscribed on

One of the many howitzers visible at the level of hold no. 4

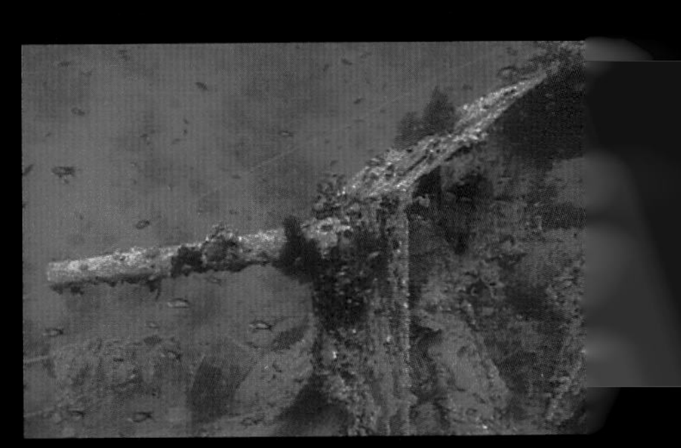

The 4.7-inch (119-mm) light anti-aircraft gur located in front of the machine gur

THE ANTI-AIRCRAFT

The armament of the *Thistlegorm* consisted of a small 10.3 inch (40 millimeters) anti-aircraft gun as well as the 4.7 inch (119 millimeters) machine-gun.

The wreck of the Thistlegorm

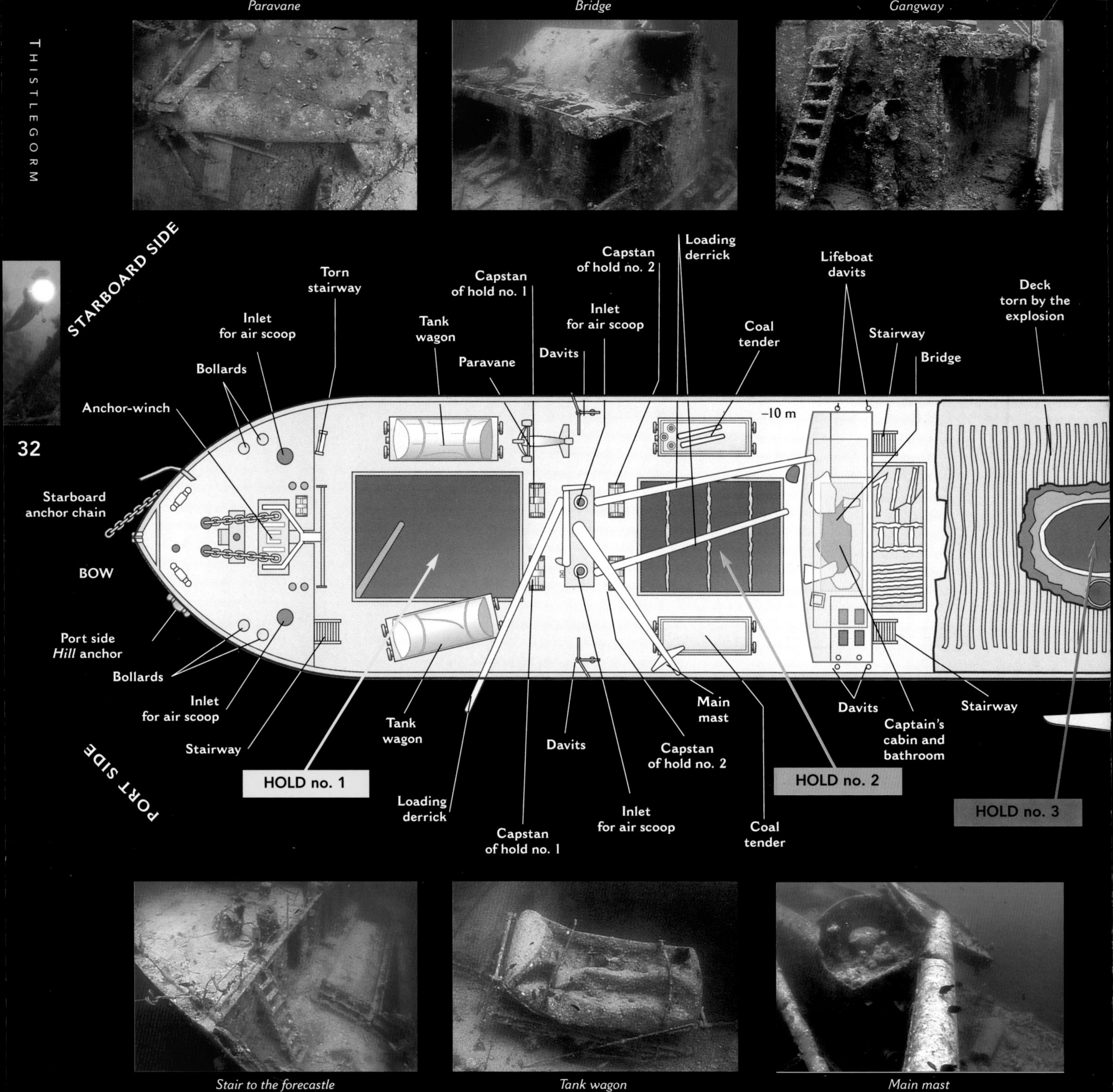
Paravane
Bridge
Gangway
STARBOARD SIDE
Torn stairway
Capstan of hold no. 1
Capstan of hold no. 2
Loading derrick
Lifeboat davits
Deck torn by the explosion
Inlet for air scoop
Tank wagon
Inlet for air scoop
Coal tender
Stairway
Bollards
Paravane
Davits
Bridge
Anchor-winch
–10 m
Starboard anchor chain
BOW
Port side Hill anchor
Bollards
Inlet for air scoop
Stairway
Tank wagon
Main mast
Davits
Captain's cabin and bathroom
Stairway
Davits
Capstan of hold no. 2
PORT SIDE
HOLD no. 1
Loading derrick
Capstan of hold no. 1
Inlet for air scoop
Coal tender
HOLD no. 2
HOLD no. 3
Stair to the forecastle
Tank wagon
Main mast

Bren Carrier MK II *tank*

Anti-aircraft gun

Stern

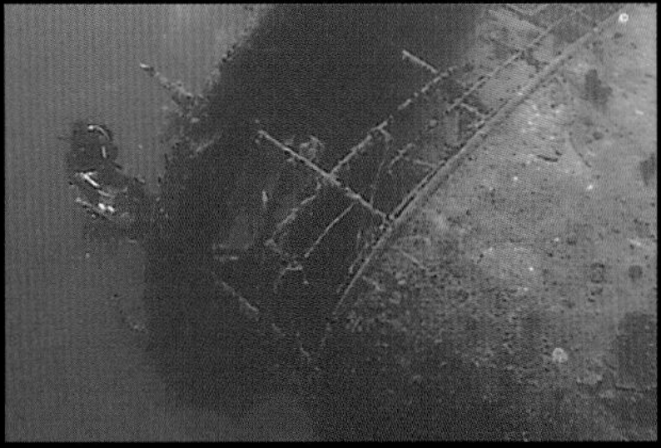

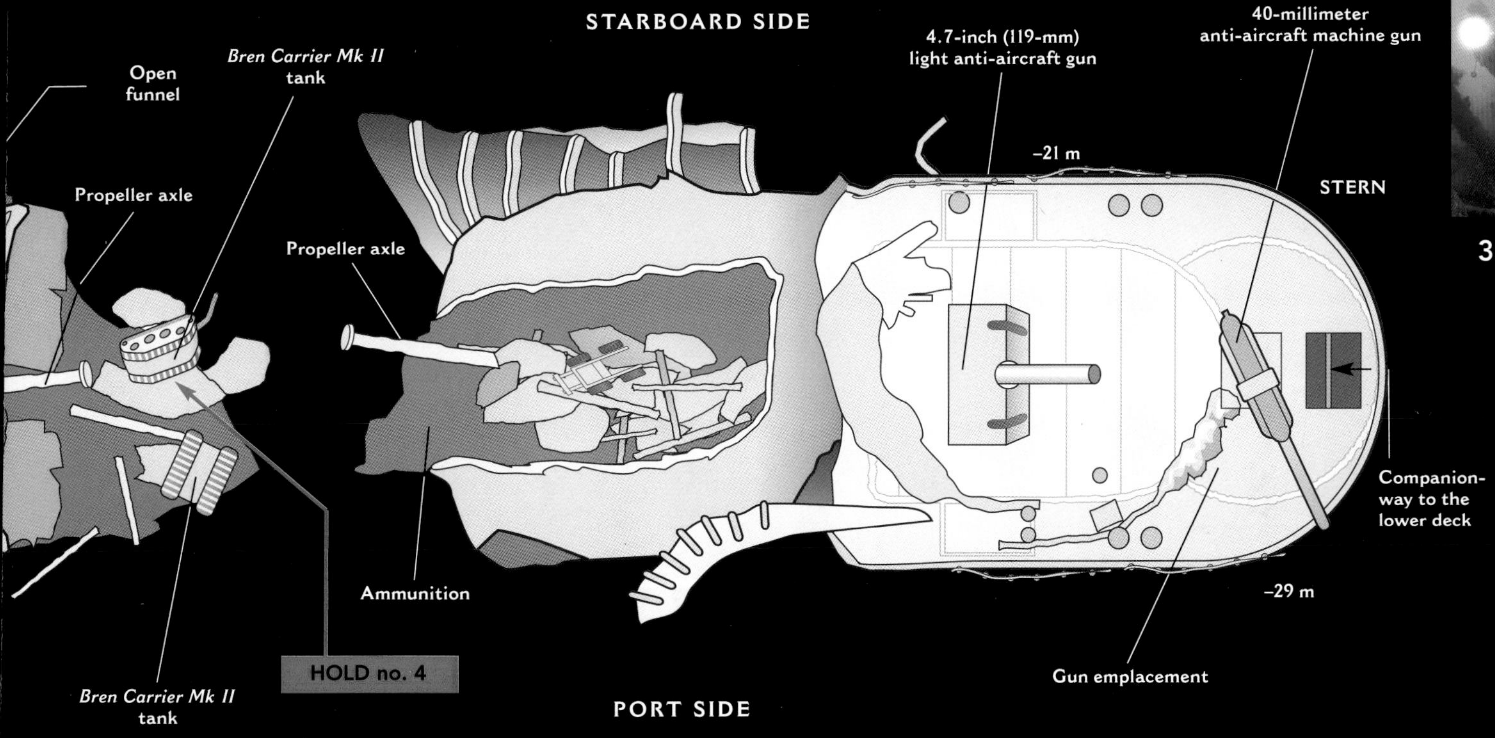

STARBOARD SIDE

Open funnel

Bren Carrier Mk II tank

4.7-inch (119-mm) light anti-aircraft gun

40-millimeter anti-aircraft machine gun

–21 m

STERN

Propeller axle

Propeller axle

Companion-way to the lower deck

Ammunition

–29 m

HOLD no. 4

Gun emplacement

Bren Carrier Mk II tank

PORT SIDE

Ammunition

Anti-aircraft machine gun

Four-bladed propeller

THE *UNIVERSAL CARRIERS MK II* TANKS

The Thistlegorm*'s cargo also included two* Universal Carrier MK II *tanks; they are overturned but still clearly visible, at the level of hold no. 4, which was struck by German bombs.*
They are small tracked vehicles with 8-cylinder, 85-horse power Ford *motors that could reach a maximum speed of 48 kilometers per hour. These armored vehicles were so versatile in action that they were dubbed "universal carriers" and used to transport men and materials.*
The Universal Carriers *were armed with one or two 7.69-millimeter* Bren Guns, *which is why they were also called "Bren Carriers."*

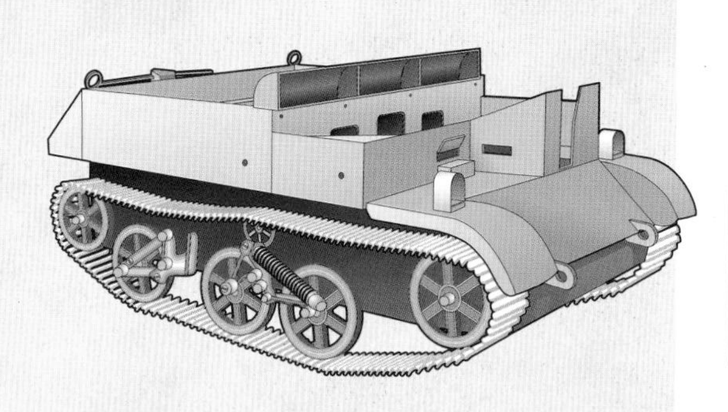

SPECIFICATIONS
Weight *4.013 tons*
Length *3.72 m*
Height *1.58 m*
Engine Ford V-8
Output *85 hp*
Maximum speed *48 km/h*

A Universal Carrier MK II *in action during a military parade*

The Universal Carrier MK II *had a crew of three and very versatile weaponry*

which only the front portion of the boiler and the first two pairs of wheels have survived, is almost parallel to that of the ship.
Moving along the hull toward the bow one comes to an open funnel vent

The first tank lies on its side

The second tank is completely overturned

Detail of the tracks and wheel mechanisms of one of the two tanks

The first locomotive is positioned some thirty meters from the ship's port side. The hatch of its boiler is closed and two pairs of wheels have survived

The shaded area of the drawing corresponds to what remains of the two Stanier 8 F *locomotives today. The explosion destroyed the cab and the rear of the boiler*

Detail of the front wheels of the first locomotive

Wheels belonging to the second locomotive, located roughly 30 meters from it

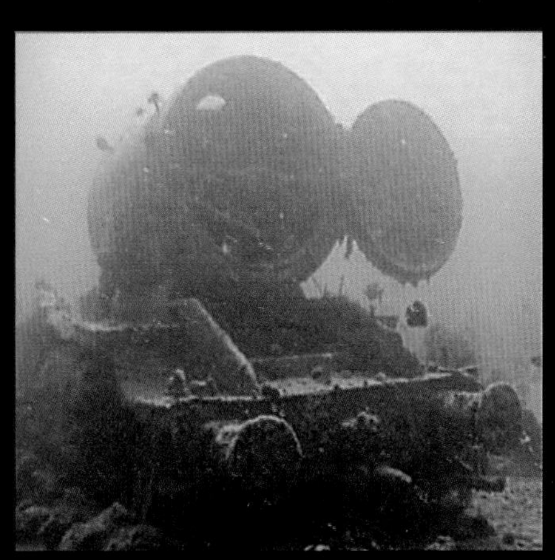

The open hatch of the boiler of the second locomotive, located to starboard of the ship

THE *STANIER 8 F* LOCOMOTIVES

The Stanier 8 F *was the most widely-used steam engine in England in the years preceding World War II.*
It was named after its inventor Sir William Stanier, who developed it in 1933.
These new-generation locomotives had particularly efficient boilers that reached a steam capacity of no less than 1,620 horse power, guaranteeing a speed of 65 kilometers per hour.
The Thistlegorm *was carrying two such locomotives on deck, equipped with coal-tenders and tank wagons to ensure the necessary water supply.*
When the ship exploded, the locomotives were flung some thirty meters from the hull, while the tenders and tank wagons remained in situ on the ship's foredeck.
Some of these locomotives remained in service through the early 1980s, and many of the old engines are still in working order today.

SPECIFICATIONS
Weight *126.7 tons*
Length *19.2 m*
Water reserve *19 tons*
Coal reserve *9 tons*
Boiler pressure *15.8 bars*
Output *1,620 hp*
Maximum speed *65 km/h*

The first Stanier 8 F *locomotive lies at a depth of 30 meters to port of the* Thistlegorm

The small stairway leading to the bridge, flanked by an air scoop

The captain's bathtub

amidst the torn wreckage of the deck. Also located here is the opening to hold no. 3, which held mainly coal. Coming to the central and highest section of the ship, we find the bridge, from which all the contents have been removed, including the on-board telegraph used to transmit orders to the engine room. Next to it is the captain's cabin, with its famous "bathroom," whose bathtub has survived complete with faucets,

The highest part of the bridge with the captain's cabin

The faucets of the basin in the captain's bathroom

though their handles are missing. Further forward is the large opening to hold no. 2, flanked by the locomotives' two coal tenders. At the level of the opening of hold no. 2, some dozens of meters to starboard, past the coal tender and at a depth of 30 meters, lies the second *Stanier 8 F* locomotive, whose major axis is roughly at a 45° angle to that of the ship. This locomotive differs from the first in that the front hatch of its boiler is open.

The second locomotive seen from above; the arrow points to the open boiler hatch

Some 30 meters aft of the locomotive lies its front pair of wheels.
Continuing along the main deck of the ship toward the bow, one notes the two large capstans of the loading derricks serving hold no. 2, and the tilted main mast, partially supported by the port side tender.
When the ship sank, the mast was still in its original position, its top nearly reaching the water's surface. It was not until the early 1970s that divers felled it with explosives, the aim being both to eliminate a possible shipping hazard and to conceal the presence of the wreck.
Next comes the quarterdeck, where we find the openings in which the large air scoops that provided ventilation for the holds were installed. There are also two further capstans before the entrance to hold no. 1, which is flanked by the two tank wagons used to transport the water supply necessary for the locomotives.

One of the two pairs of capstans that served the loading derricks of the holds

The divergent paravane, often falsely referred to as a "torpedo," is situated on the starboard side

On both sides of the deck, next to the quarterdeck, there were two torpedo-shaped paravanes fitted at the back with direction-indicator fins, and the respective davits for lifting and lowering them into the water.
Towed by the ship, these paravanes served to cut the cables fastening any potential deep-sea mines to the seabed. The paravane at starboard remains on the wreck, but only fragments of the other have survived.
Moving on toward the bow, two small stairways leading to the forecastle (whose highest point is at a depth of 16 meters) can be noted.
While the stairway at starboard was torn away in 2001 by a guide who had attached the line of his boat to it, the stairway at port was spared. Near the latter, one can observe a sea anemone

surrounded by its Red Sea anemonefish (*Amphiprion bicinctus*). Between the two small stairways, there are various doors that permit access to the forepeak, where the anchor chains and mooring lines are located.
At the center of the forecastle is the perfectly preserved large anchor winch, surrounded by dense shoals of Scalefin anthias (*Pseudanthias squamipinnis*). One may also observe the port side anchor (a *Hill* anchor), still in its original position, and its counterpart on the starboard side, which lies on the seabed over a hundred meters from the hull.
The lifeline that once spanned the entire bow has been almost completely torn away.

The large bollards to which the mooring lines were sometimes fastened

The large anchor winch located at the bow

The small stairway on the port side leading to the forecastle

One of the two water tank wagons flanking the opening to hold no. 1

One of the inlets for the air scoops located on the quarterdeck, which provided ventilation for the holds

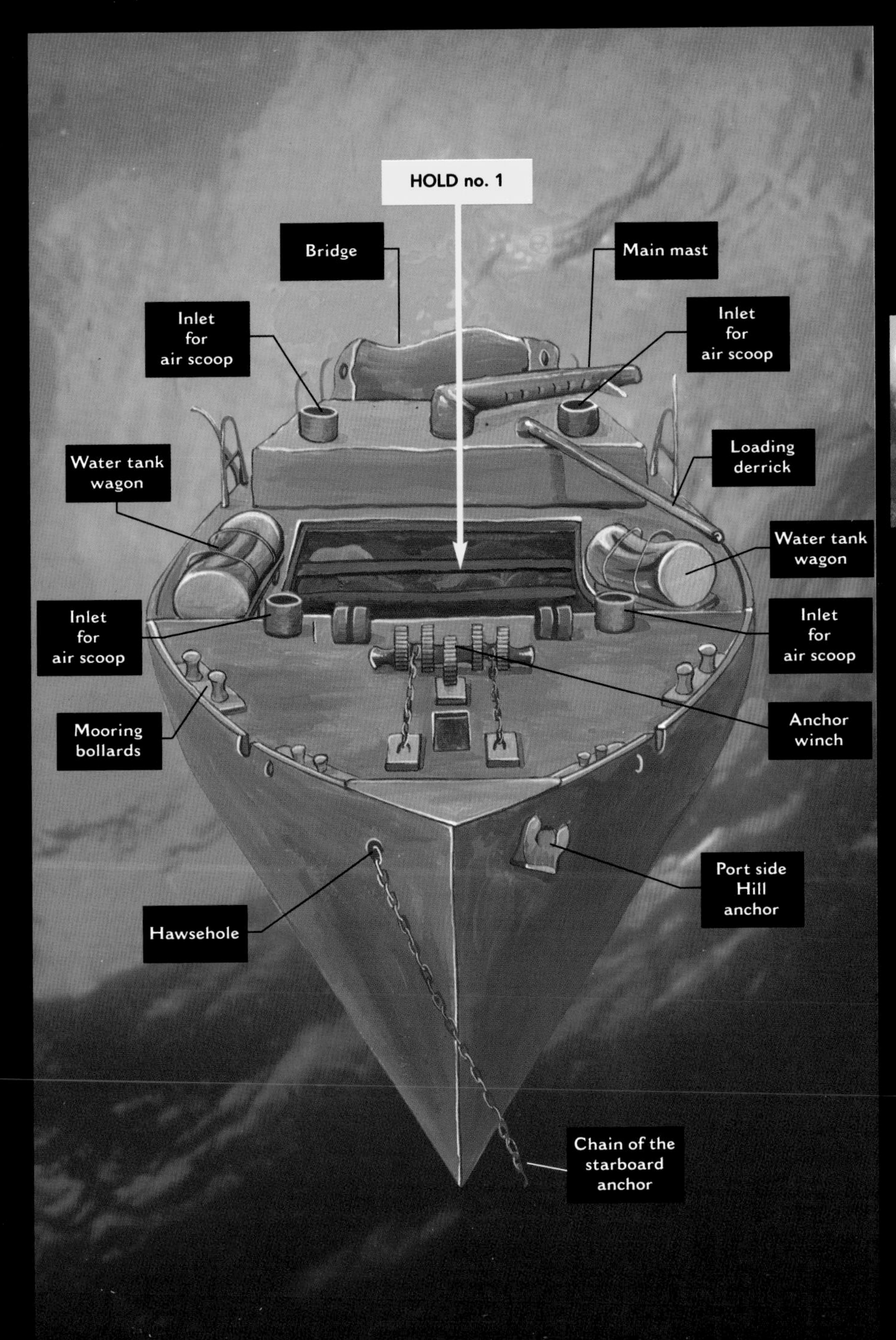

The Holds

A group of BSA *motorcycles on the back of a* Ford *truck*

Hold no. 3 is of minimal interest since it contained mainly coal for the engine boiler. If the current is strong, going through this hold is the easiest way to reach hold no. 2, which is far more interesting.
Hold no. 2 is divided into two levels: the upper and lower.
On both sides of the upper level there are *Ford WOT 2* and *Bedford 0Y* trucks, as well as several *Morris Commercial CS 8* jeeps.
There are also some *BSA W-M20* and *Norton 16 H* motorcycles, some with sidecars. On the port side of the lower level there are many trailers (almost all of which are empty) and spare airplane wings; on the starboard side there are *Bedford* trucks containing several motorcycles, a *Tilling Stevens TS-19* truck, some *Norton 16 H* motorcycles with sidecars, a supply of rubber boots, some *Lee Enfield MK III* rifles, and a large number of tires for motor vehicles.
Hold no. 1, located at the bow and

Some airplane wings in hold no. 2

The Tilling Stevens TS-19 *truck in hold no. 2*

One of the numerous empty trailers that occupy large parts of hold no. 1

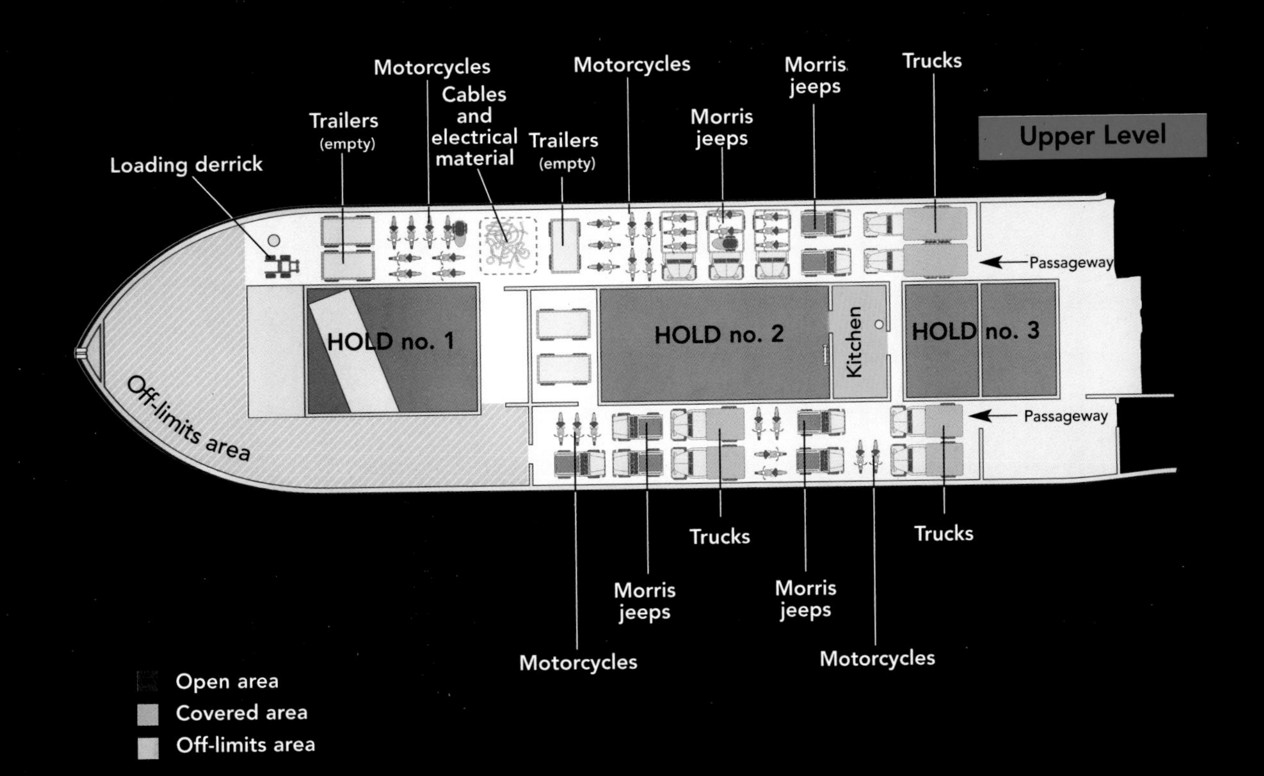

Upper Level
Loading derrick
Trailers (empty)
Motorcycles
Cables and electrical material
Trailers (empty)
Motorcycles
Morris jeeps
Morris jeeps
Trucks
Passageway
HOLD no. 1
HOLD no. 2
Kitchen
HOLD no. 3
Passageway
Off-limits area
Trucks
Trucks
Morris jeeps
Morris jeeps
Motorcycles
Motorcycles
Open area
Covered area
Off-limits area

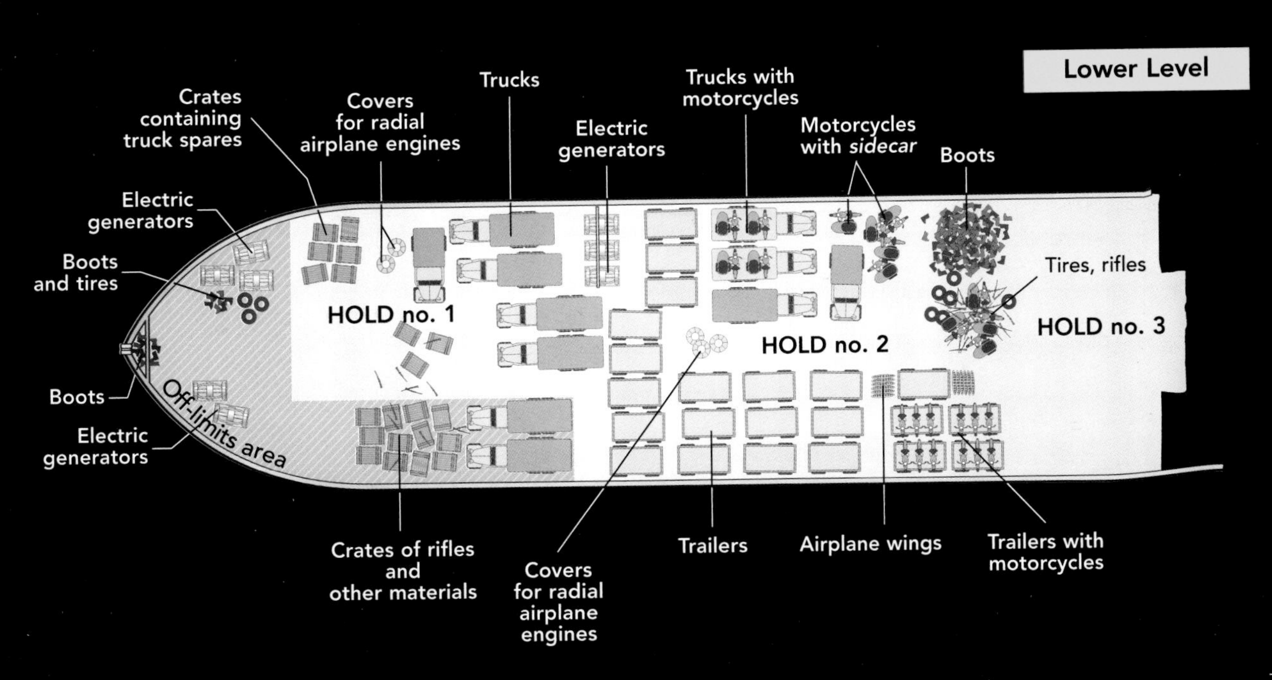

Lower Level
Crates containing truck spares
Covers for radial airplane engines
Trucks
Electric generators
Trucks with motorcycles
Motorcycles with sidecar
Boots
Electric generators
Boots and tires
Tires, rifles
HOLD no. 1
HOLD no. 2
HOLD no. 3
Boots
Off-limits area
Electric generators
Crates of rifles and other materials
Covers for radial airplane engines
Trailers
Airplane wings
Trailers with motorcycles

Exploring the Holds

The holds of the wreck are easily accessible and still contain their cargo. Divers move around automobiles, trailers, motorcycles, rifles, boots and spare parts.

The wreck of the Thistlegorm

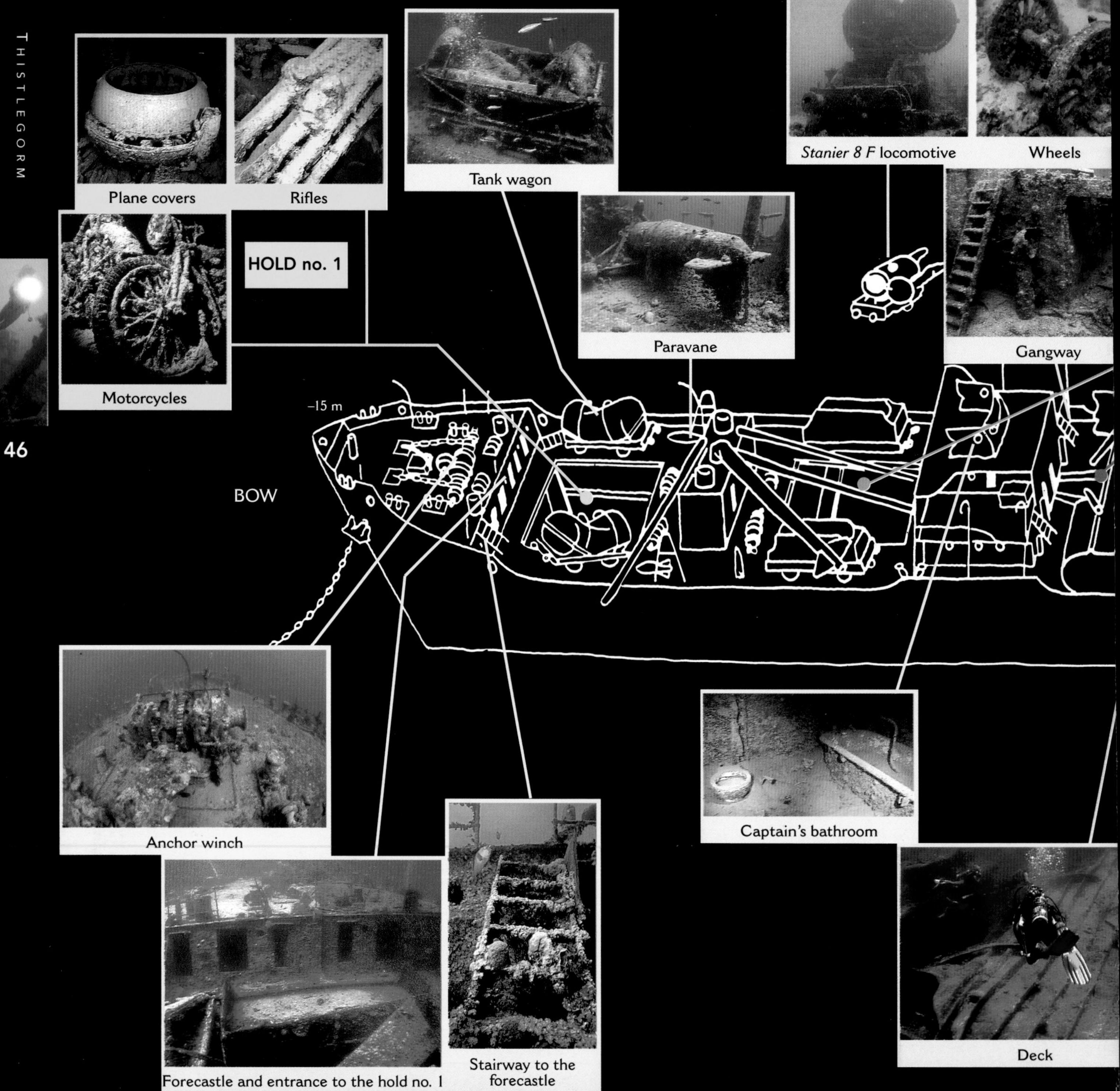
Plane covers
Rifles
Tank wagon
Stanier 8 F locomotive
Wheels
HOLD no. 1
Paravane
Gangway
Motorcycles
–15 m
BOW
Anchor winch
Forecastle and entrance to the hold no. 1
Stairway to the forecastle
Captain's bathroom
Deck

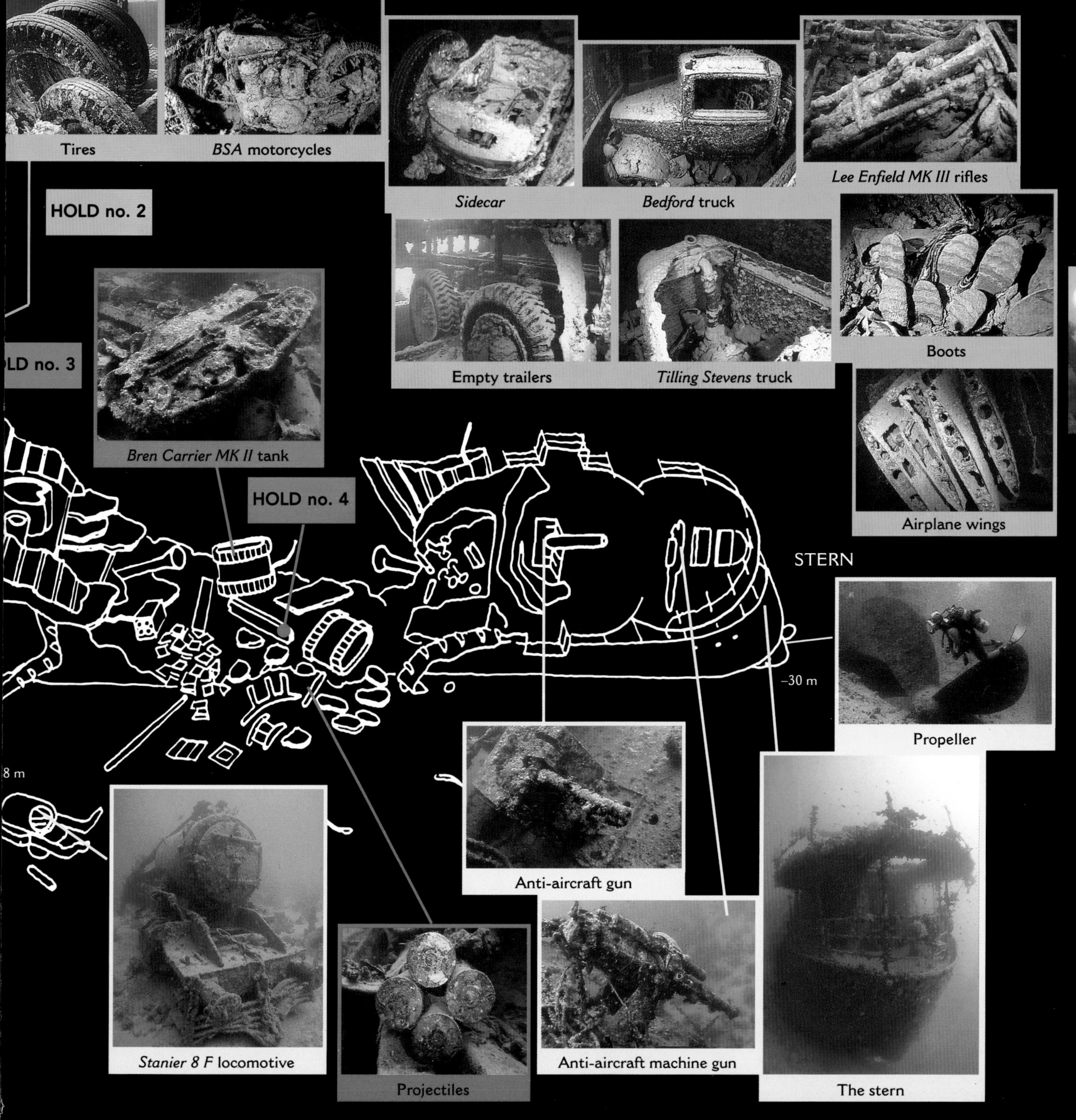
Tires
BSA motorcycles
Sidecar
Bedford truck
Lee Enfield MK III rifles
HOLD no. 2
Empty trailers
Tilling Stevens truck
Boots
LD no. 3
Bren Carrier MK II tank
Airplane wings
HOLD no. 4
STERN
–30 m
Propeller
8 m
Anti-aircraft gun
Stanier 8 F locomotive
Projectiles
Anti-aircraft machine gun
The stern

THE MOTORCYCLES

The Thistlegorm *was carrying a large number of motorcycles including* BSA *mod.* W-M20s, Norton 16 Hs, *and* Matchless G3Ls.
The BSA *(Birmingham Small Arms, the name of the manufacturing company) mod.* W-M20s *were solid motorcycles built for the desert and intended both for convoy outriders, and to transport dispatches and documents. Between 1939 and 1940, over 126,000 such motorcycles were produced.*
The Norton 16 Hs *were similar in design to the* BSAs *and many were equipped with a sidecar.*
The third group of motorcycles on board the Thistlegorm *consisted of* Matchless G3Ls, *which had the same piston displacement and output as the* Norton 16Hs.
Also designed for the desert, Matchless *motorcycles continued to be produced for civilian use after the war.*

MATCHLESS G3L
Weight *148 kg*
Engine Matchless *347 cc*
Output *16 hp*

BSA W-M20
Weight *176 kg*
Engine BSA *496 cc*
Output *12 hp*
Maximum speed *about 110 km/h*

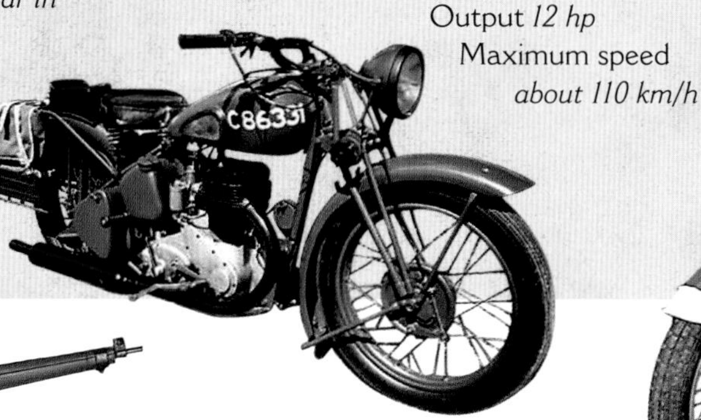

NORTON 16 H
Weight *148 kg*
Engine Matchless *347 cc*
Output *16 hp*

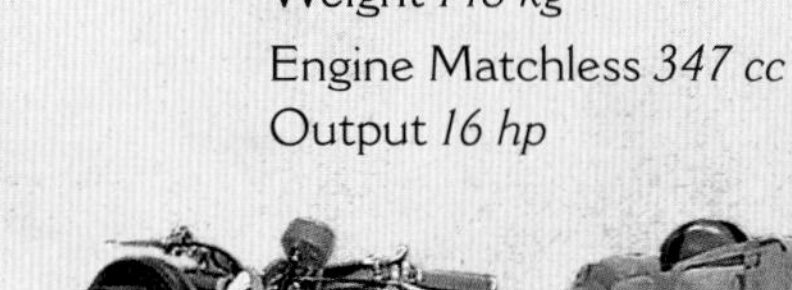

Lee Enfield MK III *rifle*

connected by two internal lateral passageways to hold no. 2, is also of considerable interest. While its port side has completely collapsed, the starboard side of this hold contains, on the upper level, two empty trailers side-by-side, *Matchless G3L* and *Norton 16 H* motorcycles (some with sidecars), and, on the lover level, covers for airplane engines, crates of medicines, *Lee Enfield MK III* rifles, and several portable electric generators.

These spare covers were for radial airplane engines

Some of the many Lee Enfield MKIII *rifles that can be seen in the* Thistlegorm *to this day*

Several BSA *motorcycles on* Bedford *trucks in hold no. 2 of the* Thistlegorm

THE TRUCKS

A substantial part of the Thistlegorm*'s cargo consisted of small trucks of various kinds, mostly to be found in hold no. 2.*
There are several Ford WOT 2s, *versatile trucks with a canvas-covered back; some 60,000 of these were built during World War II. Similar to these, but much bigger, were the* Ford WOT 3s; *18,000 of these were produced.*
Even larger were the Ford WOT 1s *which were 6.49 meters long and whose three axles set them apart from all the other trucks; one of these is to be found on the lower level of hold no. 2. This is an extremely rare truck (the British army had only just over a hundred of them); it was used to transport heavy loads and for a wide variety of other purposes (as a platform for anti-aircraft reflectors, as an ambulance, and as a support for electric generators, etc.).*

FORD WOT 2
Weight *2.034 kg*
Length *4,49 m*
Height *2,28 m*
Engine Ford *8 cylinders of 3,621 cc*
Output *60 hp*

TILLING STEVENS TS-19
Weight *4,091 kg*
Length *6.35 m*
Height *3.30 m*
Engine Tilling Stevens *6 cylinders of 5,115 cc*
Output *70 hp*

The Tilling Stevens TS-19 *truck was similar in size but only had two axles; one of these is also to be found in hold no. 2.*

BEDFORD MW
Weight *2,128 kg*
Length *4.36 m*
Height *2.28 m*
Engine Bedford *6 cylinders of 3,519 cc*
Output *72 hp*

There are a larger number of Bedford MWs *(easily identifiable by their cabs, made of thin sheet iron and generally open) and* Bedford OYs, *versatile vehicles used widely by the British army, of which more than 72,000 were produced.*
Finally, there are also several examples of the Morris Commercial CS 8 *jeep, with its 6-cylinder engine and typical angular hood, which is its distinguishing feature.*

MORRIS COMMERCIAL CS 8
Weight *Unknown*
Length *4.49 m*
Height *2.28 m*
Engine Ford *8 cylinders of 3,621 cc*
Output *25 hp*

BEDFORD OY
Weight *2,673 kg*
Length *6.22 m*
Height *3.10 m*
Engine Bedford *6 cylinders of 3,519 cc*
Output *72 hp*

AUTOMOBILES ON BOARD

The driver's seat of a *Morris Commercial* CS 8 jeep: the steering-wheel, gearshift, and brake are still in good condition

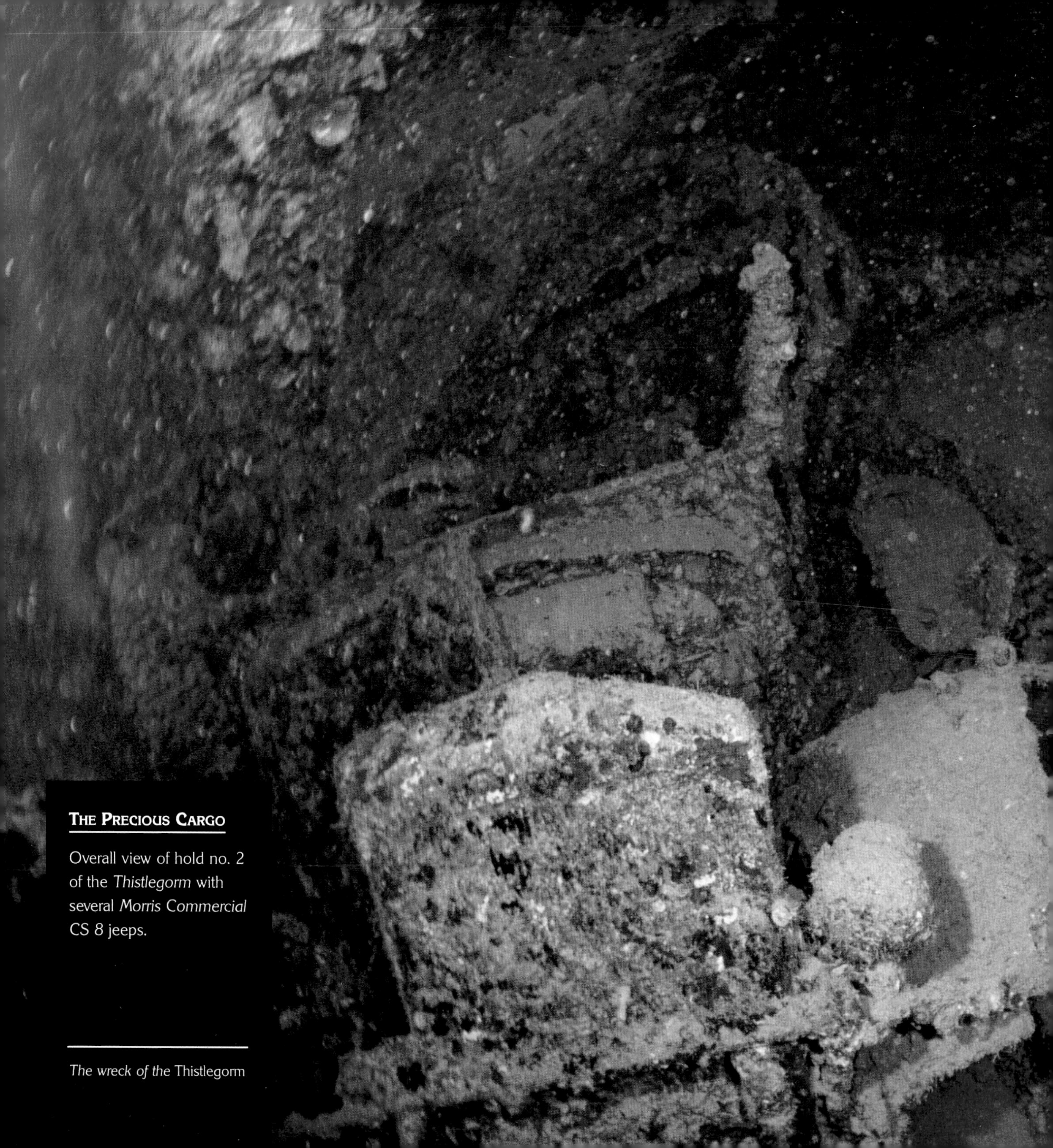

THE PRECIOUS CARGO

Overall view of hold no. 2 of the *Thistlegorm* with several *Morris Commercial* CS 8 jeeps.

The Fauna of the *Thistlegorm*

In the years immediately after it sank, the *Thistlegorm* was rapidly colonized by soft and stony corals, turning it into a veritable artificial reef inhabited by a great variety of fauna. In recent years, however, the excessive number of scuba divers has drastically reduced the soft corals, especially the Alcyonacea, which have virtually disappeared.

Nevertheless, the fauna of the *Thistlegorm* remains very varied and consists both of fish that are to be found throughout the whole wreck, and others that have chosen to live in particular sections of it, probably because these are the habitats best suited to them. The large Flathead crocodilefish (*Papilloculiceps longiceps*) that lives on deck is a familiar figure. At the stern and gangway, large shoals of glassfish or Red Sea dwarf sweepers (*Parapriacanthus ransonneti*) can frequently be found, with a solitary Redmouth grouper (*Aethaloperca rogaa*) swimming among them. Shoals of batfish (*Platax orbicularis* and *P. teira*) also circle the stern and bow, while Common lionfish (*Pterois miles*)

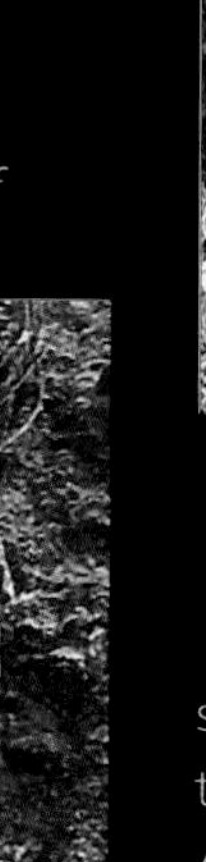

Many nudibranchs (genus Chromodoris*) like this one can be seen in the* Thistlegorm

An anemone with its Red Sea anemonefish lives near the foot of the small stairway leading to the forecastle

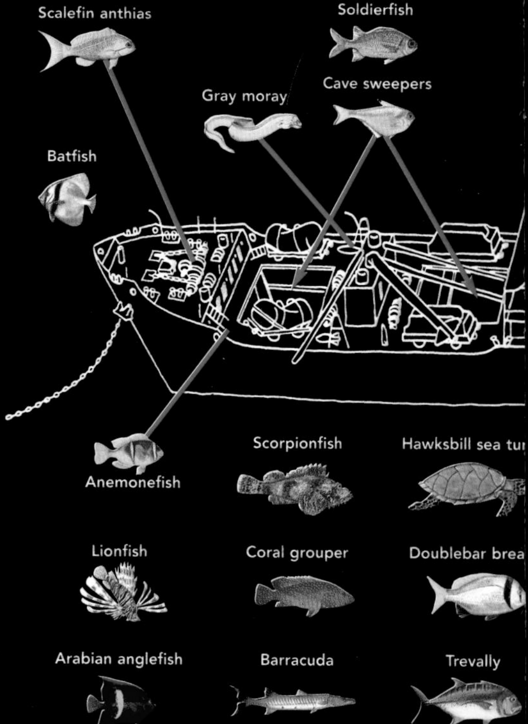

Encrusting anemones can frequently be found on the wreck's metal cables

This Flathead crocodilefish (Papiloculiceps longiceps) *lives on the* Thistlegorm*'s deck*

swim about the gangway and in recesses sheltered from the current and light, often on the hunt for small prey, especially glassfish. Shoals of Scalefin anthias (*Pseudanthias squamipinnis*) inhabit the shallower areas where the current is stronger, particularly near the anchor winch, where they can be seen frantically

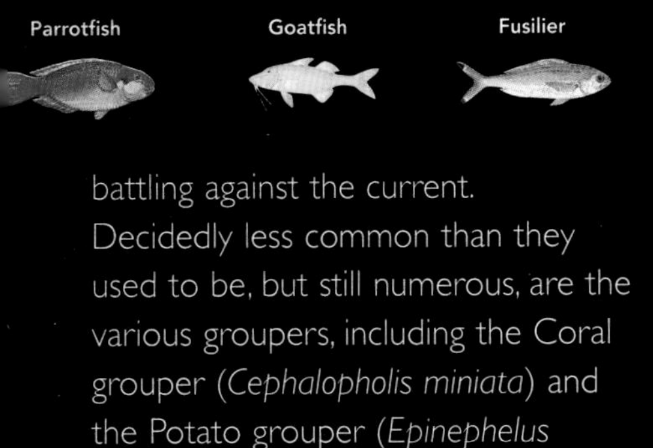

battling against the current. Decidedly less common than they used to be, but still numerous, are the various groupers, including the Coral grouper (*Cephalopholis miniata*) and the Potato grouper (*Epinephelus tukula*), which favors the area where

A Doublebar bream (Acanthopagrus bifasciatus)

the propeller and rudder are located. Doublebar breams (*Acanthopagrus bifasciatus*) can be seen here and there, but are especially common in the enclosed spaces, while the deepest areas of the holds are predominantly inhabited by Saber squirrelfish (*Sargocentron spiniferum*) circling among the trucks and empty trailers, Cave sweepers (*Pempheris vanicolensis*), and White-edged soldierfish (*Myripristis murdjan*). Sheltered areas are home to

A Coral grouper (Cephalopholis miniata)

several Giant morays (*Gymnothorax javanicus*) and some small Gray morays (*Siderea grisea*), one of which has chosen to live inside the paravane. Around the wreck, one can see groups of emperorfish (genus *Lethrinus*), several solitary Arabian angelfish (*Pomacanthus maculosus*), easy to recognize by its large yellow triangular patch whose shape resembles that of Sinai, and occasionally schools of Great barracuda (*Sphyraena barracuda*) and Giant trevallies (*Caranx ignobilis*).

A Potato grouper (Epinephelus tukula)

A group of emperorfish (genus Letrinus*)*

A small Gray moray (Siderea grisea) *inside the paravane*

Even a few Giant morays (Gymnothorax javanicus) *live in the recesses of the wreck*

A Bullethead parrotfish (Scarus sordidus) *feeds on the encrustations covering the hull*

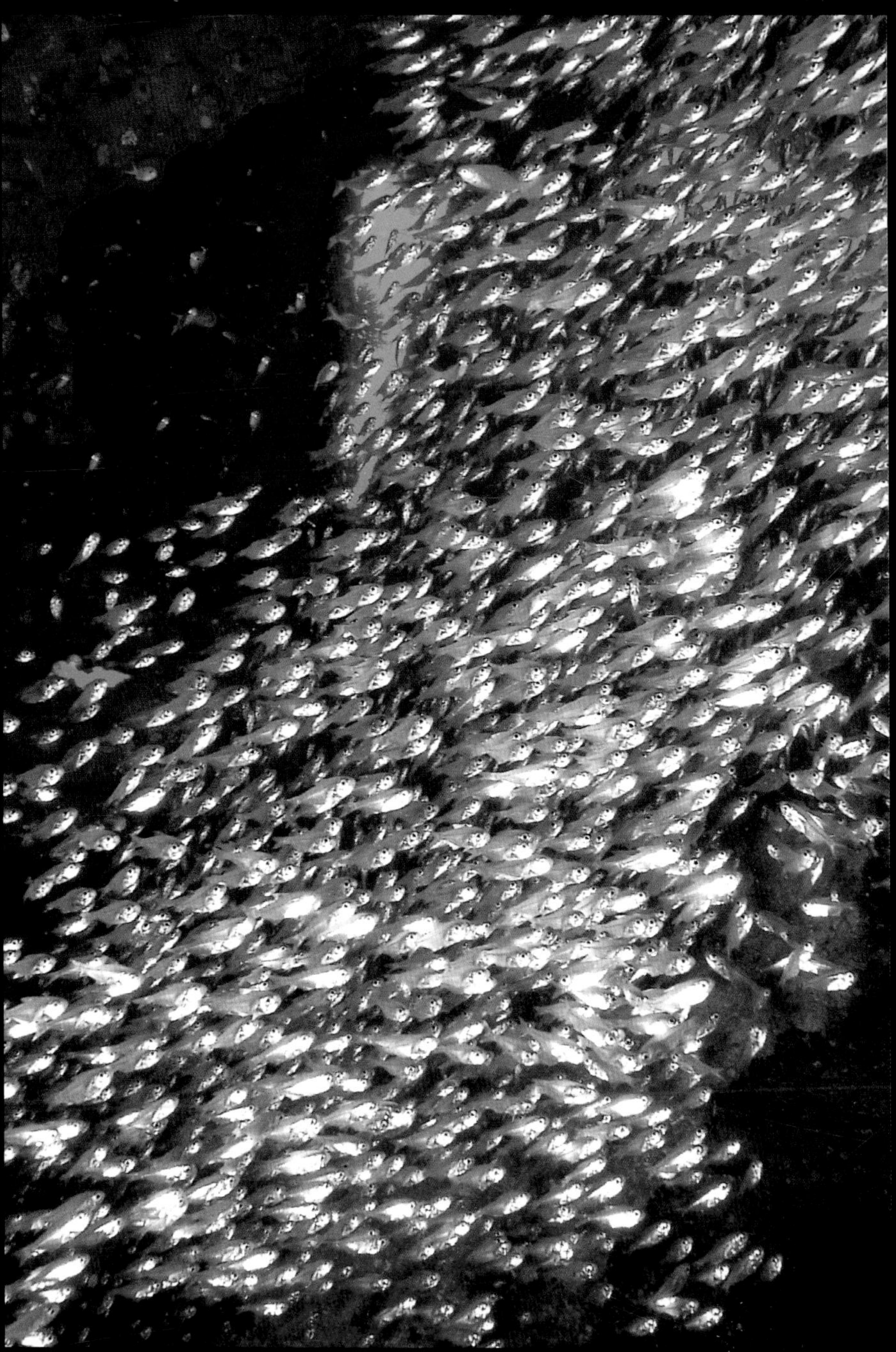

Scuba divers exploring the Thistlegorm *are often surrounded by dense shoals of glassfish or Red Sea dwarf sweepers* (Parapriacanthus ransonneti)

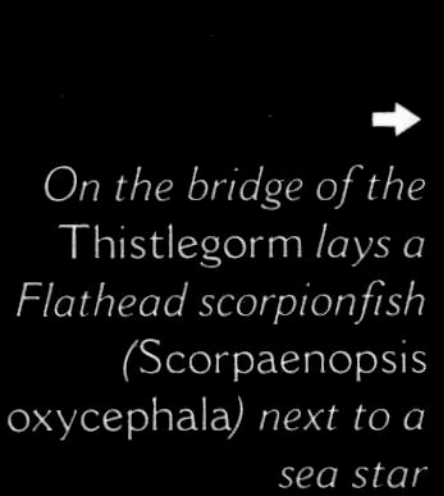

On the bridge of the Thistlegorm *lays a Flathead scorpionfish (*Scorpaenopsis oxycephala*) next to a sea star*

*Sometimes a Hawksbill turtle (*Eretmochelys imbricata*) finds shelter between the structures of the* Thistlegorm

*Over the bridge of the wreck, a school of Red Sea bannerfish (*Heniochus intermedius*) swims between the metal structures*

*A dense school of Anthias (*Pseudanthias squamipinnis*) moves around the big anchor winch at the bow*

Conservation of the Wreck

The gas tank caps of these BSA *motorcycles have been removed*

Unfortunately, the number of scuba divers who now visit the *Thistlegorm* every day has become a threat to the conservation of its iron structures; the air bubbles expelled by the divers accumulate against the metal walls, causing harmful and extremely rapid corrosion and endangering the survival of the wreck. In the course of just a few years, the excessive number of visitors has strikingly reduced the soft corals colonizing the ship.
Moreover, many inconsiderate divers have been unable to resist the temptation to pilfer objects, motorcycle parts, and even ammunition from the wreck. But the *Thistlegorm* is not only one of the most famous wrecks in the world, one of Egypt's main tourist attractions, and a major source of revenue (with its roughly 2,000 visitors a month it generates an estimated annual cash flow of approximately three million dollars, more than the pyramids of Giza); it is also, and above all, one of the most extraordinary historic relics of World War II.
Its conservation has become an urgent necessity and the Egyptian authorities should impose strict regulations on all dives or even prohibit access to the site altogether.

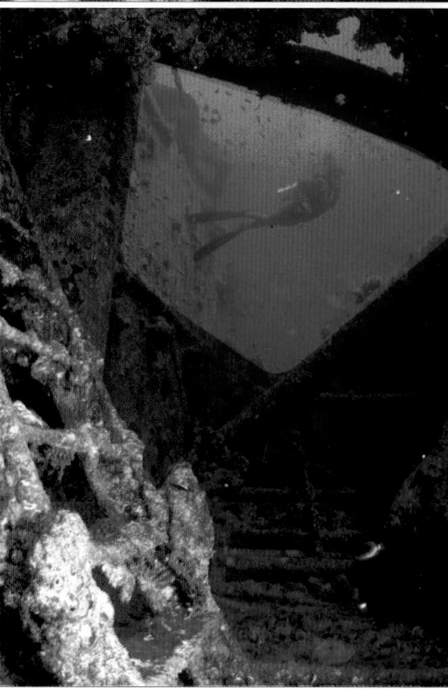

These two photos were taken seven years apart. In the later one, the beautiful Alcyonacea at the foot of the stairway has disappeared, and there is a drastic reduction in soft corals in general

One of the small stairways to the forecastle in 1993 and 2003: you can see a minor colonization of sponges and pulsing polyp corals (Xenids). Today the handrails (above in the photo) are completely destroyed

1993

2003

The radiogionometric antenna, pictured in 1955 by the expedition members of captain Cousteau. The antenna, as so many other objects of the vessel, was unscrupulously removed by divers and then donated to the "Sinai and Diving Heritage Museum," a small private museum in Naama Bay where it is currently on display

1955

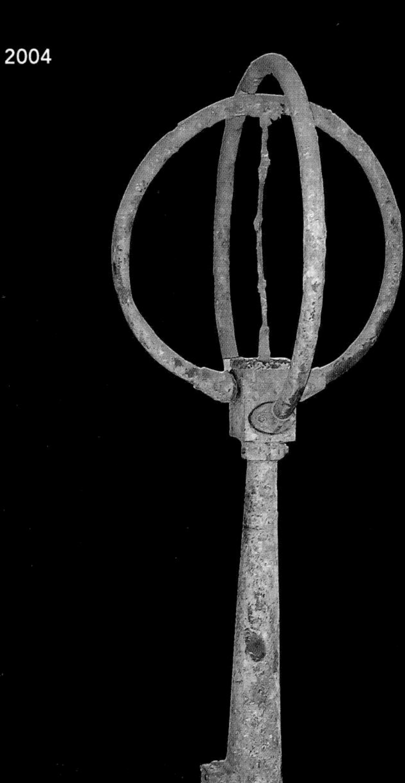
2004

THE LATEST DISCOVERY

The bow of the *Rosalie Moller*, in perfect condition, lies at a depth of 32 meters. The wreck was discovered in 1993.

The wreck of the Rosalie Moller

ROSALIE MOLLER

The History

A rare photo of the Rosalie Moller *when it was still called the* Francis

The SS ("steam ship") *Rosalie Moller*, a British freighter 108.2 meters long and 10 meters wide, that displaced 3,963 tons, was launched in January 1910 at the *Barclay Curle & Co.* shipyard in Whitenish (Glasgow) and registered under the name *Francis* in Liverpool that same year. Equipped with a three-cylinder triple expansion engine that generated an output of 1,980 horsepower, the ship could reach a maximum speed of 10.5 knots.

In 1931, the vessel was bought by the Scandinavian shipping company *Moller Line* and registered with the new name *Rosalie Moller*, under the English flag in the port of Shanghai, which was then under British control.

For several years, the *Rosalie Moller* plied the seas near eastern China, between Shanghai and Tsingtao. Then, in 1938, when war was looming, she was recalled to Liverpool to be overhauled. Quite old by this point, the *Rosalie Moller* could only travel at a reduced speed (no faster than 7.5 knots), despite the thorough overhaul of her engine in July 1941; consequently, she was assigned to transport coal to the British naval bases.

Transcript of Register for Transmission to Registrar

Official Number: 128016 — Name of Ship: Rosalie Moller

No., Date, and Port of previous Registry (if any): No. 3 in 1910, Liverpool

British or Foreign Built: British — Whether a Sailing, Steam or Motor Ship; if Steam or Motor Ship, how propelled: Steam Ship, Single Screw — Where Built: Whitenish

Number of Decks: Two & Shelter Deck
Rigged: Schooner
Stern: Elliptical
Build: Clinker
Framework and description of vessel: Steel
Number of Bulkheads: Eight
Number of water ballast tanks, and their capacity in tons: Nine = 1493 tons total

RECEIVED 29 SEP 1931 — GENERAL REGISTER & RECORD OFFICE OF SHIPPING & SEAMEN

PARTICULARS OF DISPLACEMENT
Total to quarter the depth from weather deck at side amidships to bottom of keel: 7730 Tons.

PARTICULARS OF PROPELLING ENGINES

Boilers: British, 1910, Barclay Curle & Co. Ltd, Glasgow

PARTICULARS OF TONNAGE

Gross Tonnage	No. of Tons
Under Tonnage Deck	3382·59
Space or spaces between Decks	
Turret or Trunk	
Forecastle	81·32
Bridge space	251·97
Poop or Break	56·70
Side Houses	
Deck Houses	149·57
Chart House	
Spaces for Machinery, and light, and air, under Section 78(2) of the Merchant Shipping Act, 1894	41·22
Excess of Hatchways	
Gross Tonnage	3963·37 — 11216·34
Deductions, as per contra	1506·65 — 4263·82
Register Tonnage	2456·72 — 6952·52

Name of Master: J. Korhemaker

Names, Residence, and Description of the Owners, and Number of Sixty-fourth Shares held by each, viz.,
Eric Bleckynden Moller of 12 the Bund, Shanghai
Sixty four (64) shares.
Dated 17th August, 1931, Shanghai.

C. No. 345.

Instructions to Registrars of British

Excerpt from the British Shipping Register filled out in Shanghai on 17 August 1931 – after the ship had been purchased by the Moller Line *and renamed – that shows the specifications and particulars of the* Rosalie Moller

ing and Seamen.
ort of Registry
Shanghai.
and Address of Builders
Feet | Tenths
355
355
49 2·5
24 2
27 5·2
26 6·9
by enemy
Rotary Engines
No. of Cylinders in each set
N.H.P.
I.H.P.
Speed of Ship.
June, 1923
1980
10½ knots
No. of Tons
power .... 1268·28
153·43
n accomo-
Shipping
Shipping
84·94
1506·65
the total spaces framed
ship's register tonnage :
No.
Registrar.
" against his name.
10861
1927

The Bow of the Giant

The elegant silhouette of the bow of the vessel on which can be seen the flag spreader and one of the big capstans.

The wreck of the Rosalie Moller

The Last Voyage

A Heinkel He 111 *in flight*

After leaving the port of Durban in South Africa on 11 September 1941, under the command of Captain James Byrne and carrying a load of 4,680 tons of "best Welsh coal," the *Rosalie Moller* headed for Alexandria in Egypt.

She had no problem sailing up the east coast of Africa and passing through the Strait of Bab el-Mandeb, and, after a brief stop at Aden in Southern Yemen, she crossed the Red Sea to the Strait of Gubal. During the night between 7 and 8 October, the *Rosalie Moller* was lying at anchor off the north-western part of the island of Gubal Saghir, in what was considered a safe berth code-named *Safe Anchorage H* in military reports, since the Suez Canal was still blocked by a ship that had run into a mine.

At 0:45 am on 8 October 1941, however, the *Rosalie Moller* was spotted by two German *Heinkel He 111* bombers of the *Kampfgeschwader KG 26*, the squadron stationed on the island of Crete whose planes had sunk the *Thistlegorm* two days earlier. The ship was attacked and struck by two bombs that tore into holds no. 4 and no. 5, causing the vessel to sink exactly one hour later, at 1:45 am.

The 30 members of the crew managed to save themselves, though two men lost their lives when the ship went down. The wreck remained undisturbed for more than half a century, and was only discovered in 1993. It immediately came to be referred to as a sister ship of the *Thistlegorm*, even though, in actual fact, the two vessels differ substantially: being designed some thirty years before the *Thistlegorm*, the *Rosalie Moller* is smaller (935 tons less, and 18 meters shorter in length), as well as having a structurally different hull, a more sinous line to the stern and a straighter keel. Nonetheless, when it comes to their sinking the two vessels do have some points in common: the hour of attack; the position of the vessels bombed whilst lying at starboard anchor; and the speed they sank in the night.

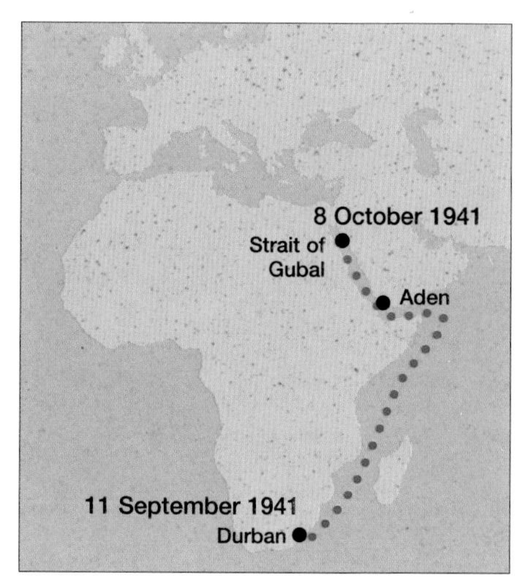

The Rosalie Moller*'s route*

6th October	"NAIAD", "ERIDGE", "AVONVALE" Suez to Alexandria. At 0035 attack by 4 Enemy aircraft on Anchorage 'F' in Gulf of Suez. "THISTLEGORM" sunk. "SALAMANA" and "NORFOLD" slight damage.
7th October	Canal closed for 48 hours owing to explosion of mine at K. 18.0 by Hopper. (South of Shab Ali) Use of Anchorage 'F' discontinued, anchorage 'H' (Towila) used instead.
8th October	0045 and 0145 attack by 2 Enemy aircraft on anchorage 'H' in Gulf of Suez. "ROSALIE MOLLER" at 'H' bombed and sunk. H.E.M.S. "AIDA" damaged at Ras Gharib by Enemy Aircraft which crashed.

Excerpt from the war diary of the British admiralship regarding the Suez area, October 1941

Tour of the Wreck

The *Rosalie Moller* lies upright at an even keel on a sandy seabed at a depth of about 50 meters. The top of her mast is 17 meters below the surface and the four-bladed propeller is at 45 meters. The bow and stern are intact and the bridge instruments are in good condition. The dive is particularly difficult because of low visibility, the almost constant current, and the considerable depth it is necessary to reach in order to explore the entire wreck.
The ship's sheet metal is almost entirely covered by a thick layer of mud and the holds still contain their cargo of coal, which is of little interest. The engine room, located at a depth of 46 meters, on the other hand, is almost completely intact, its workbench still with its vice, tools, and even oilcans still *in situ*; however, access is too difficult for amateurs and it can only be explored by expert scuba divers. It is thus advisable to visit the upper areas, located at a depth of approximately 30–35 meters, and examine the forebridge and the long bridge on which the funnel is located, marked with a huge, perfectly discernible "M," the initial of the company's name.
The funnel was in perfect condition

Aerial view of the northern area of Gubal Island and the area where the wreck of the Rosalie Moller *is located*

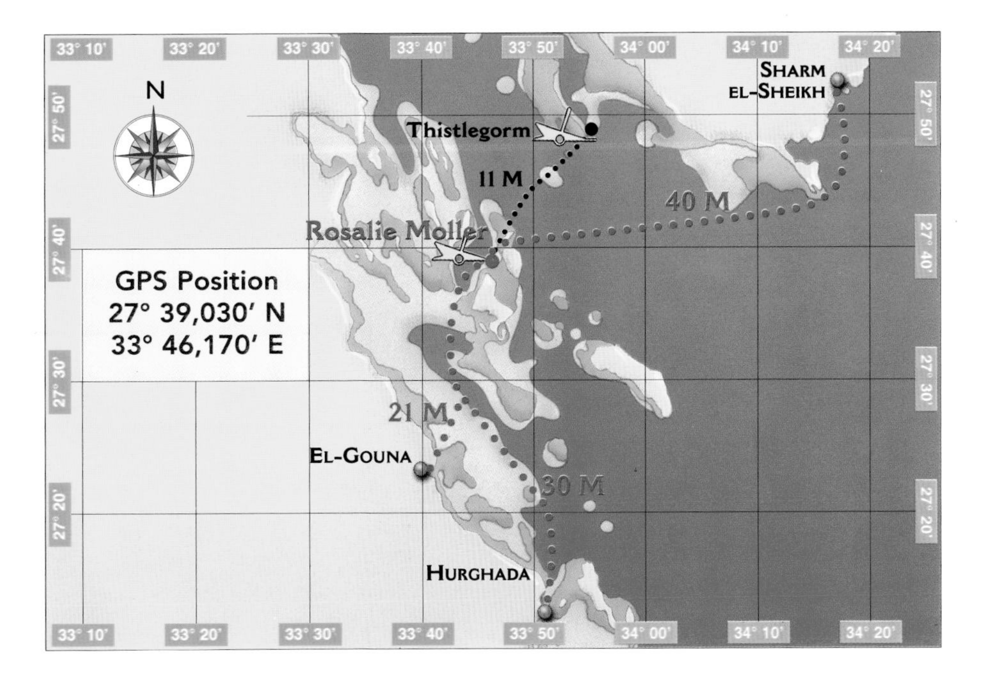

Exploring the Wreck

A group of divers swim over the central part of the vessel which sank in an upright position on the sandy seabed at an average depth of 50 meters. The fact that the wreck is located far away from big tourist centres and that it is in deep waters have contributed to its protection.

The wreck of the Rosalie Moller

N

–17 m
Stern mast
Officer accomodations
Kitchen, Caboose
Dispensary
Funnel
Letter **M**,
the shipping
company's initial
Ventilation
structure
Tank
Quaterdeck
HOLD no. 5
HOLD no. 4
HOLD no. 3
Gangway
Passageway
STERN
–45 m
Propeller
Area struck
by the bomb
–48 m

Rosalie Moller
M
SPECIFICATIONS
Type of ship Steam freighter
Nationality British
Shipping Company Moller Line Ltd
Shipyard Barclay Curle & Co. Ltd
Launching date January 1910
Length 108.2 m
Tonnage 3,963 tons
Displacement 7,730 tons
Engine output 1,980 hp
Speed 10.5 knots
–17 m
Bow mast
Bridge deck
HOLD no. 2
HOLD no. 1
Anchor winch
Forepeaks
Flagpole
Gangway
–35 m
BOW
–48 m
–53 m

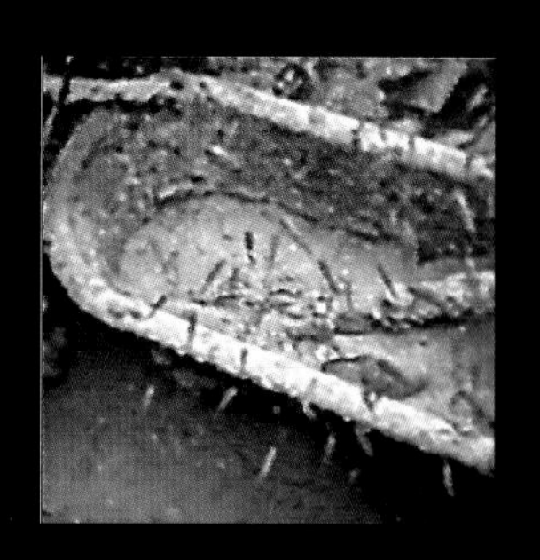

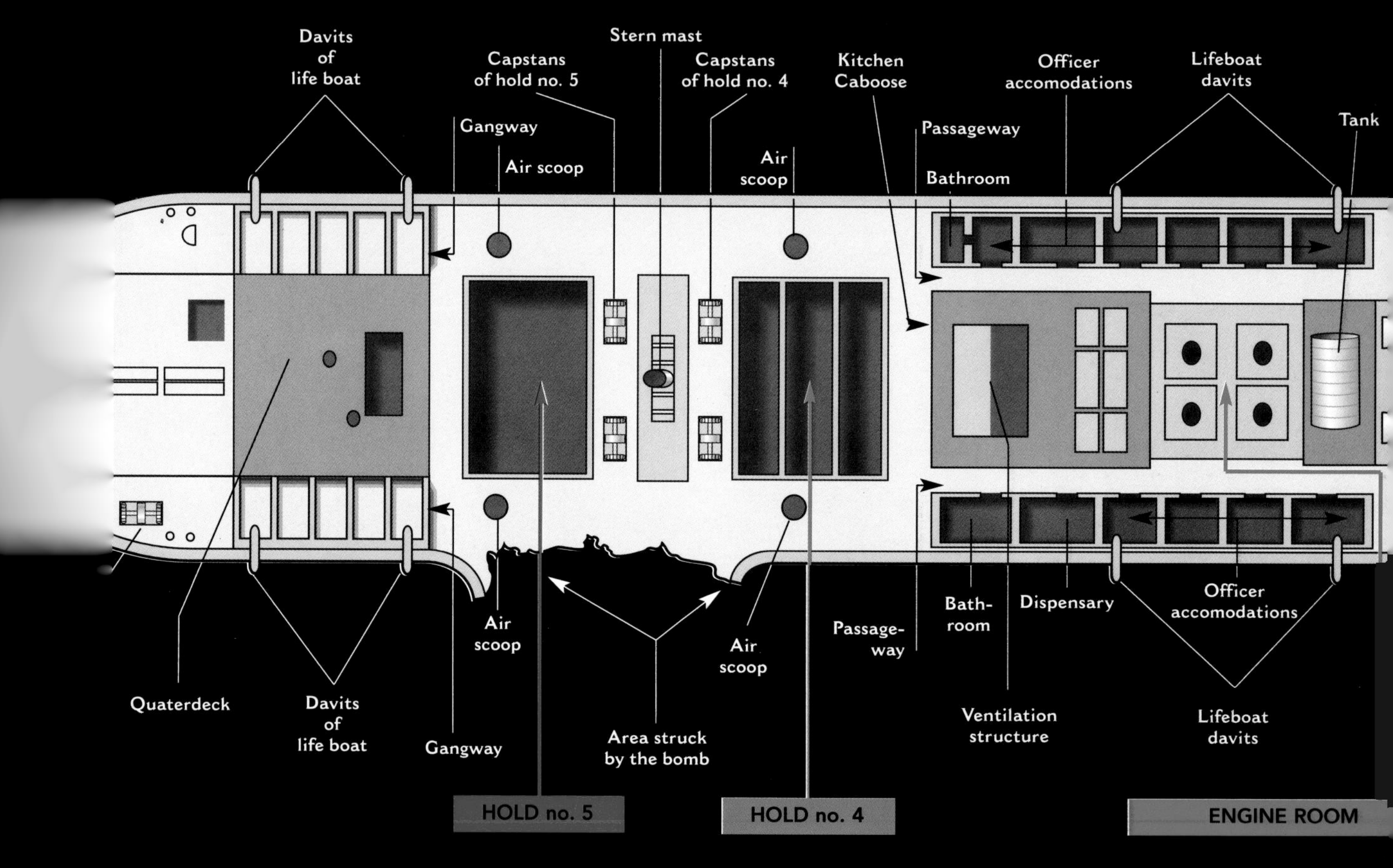

Bomb impact area

Entrance to the machine room

Companionway to the machine room

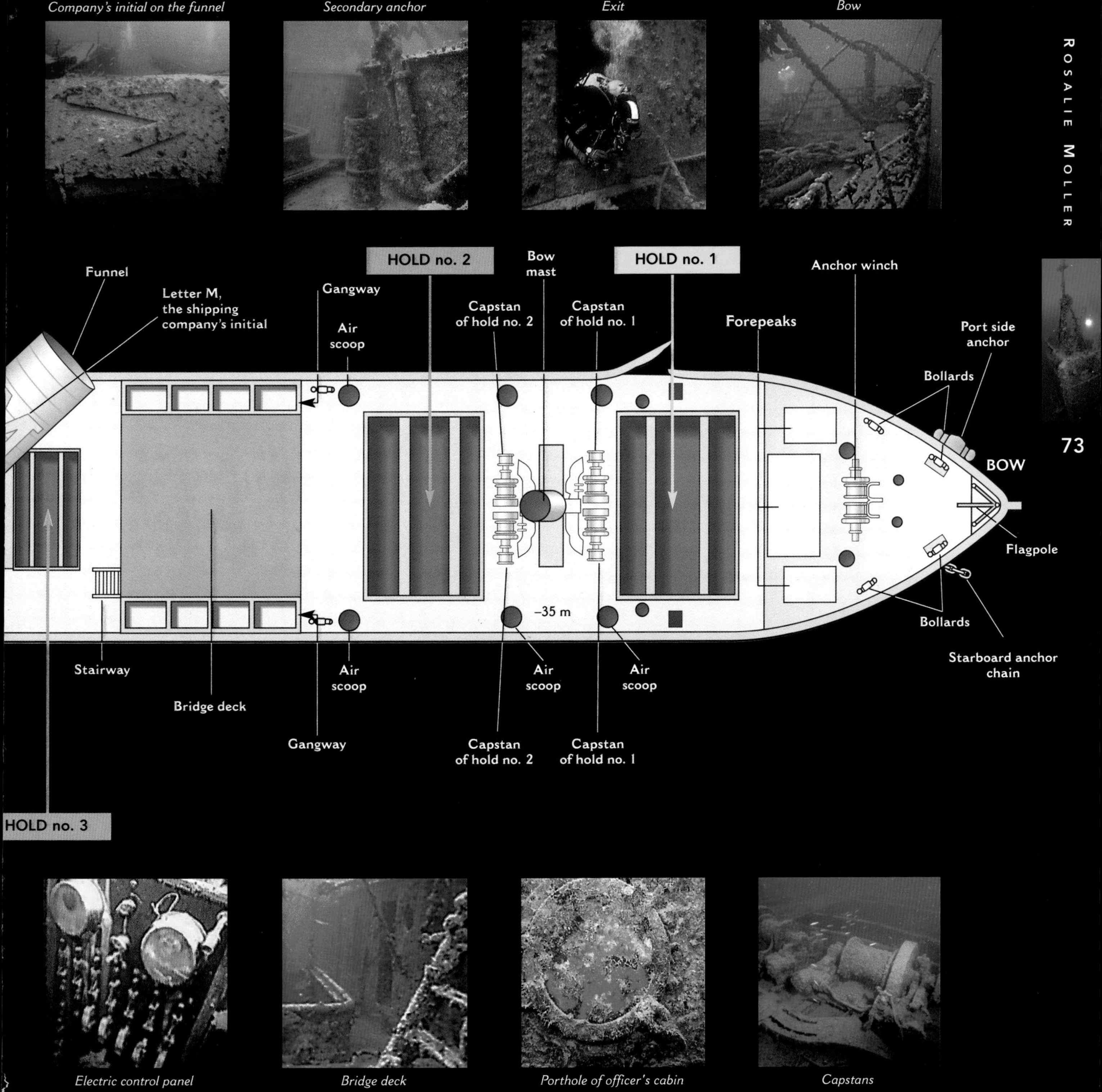

Company's initial on the funnel

Secondary anchor

Exit

Bow

Electric control panel

Bridge deck

Porthole of officer's cabin

Capstans

The two German Heinkel He III *bombers hit the* Rosalie Moller *at the level of hold no. 4 causing a wide fracture that sank the vessel quickly*

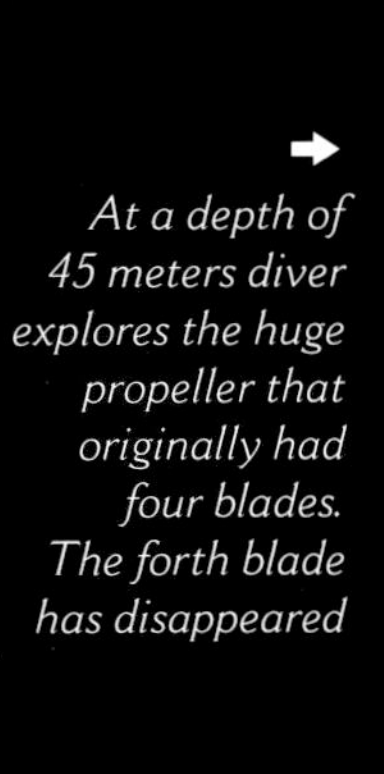

At a depth of 45 meters diver explores the huge propeller that originally had four blades. The forth blade has disappeared

The impressive anchor winch on the quarterdeck on the port side of the Rosalie Moller

In what formerly must have been a repair shop, a bench vice fixed on the lathe is still identifiable despite the coral incrustations.

*On the port side of the wreck, the anchor is visible in its original position. Around its arms a large Common bigeye (*Priacanthus hamrur*) is swimming quietly*

ROSALIE MOLLER

On both sides of the upper deck level were the officers' bathrooms: in one of these rooms, a well preserved bath tub was found with one boot in it …

The galley surprises the astonished diver: a saucepan is still hanging over the boiler plate …

The vessel's cargo of 4,680 tons of charcoal is still visible in the holds; it has taken on a yellowish colour due to the muddy deposit

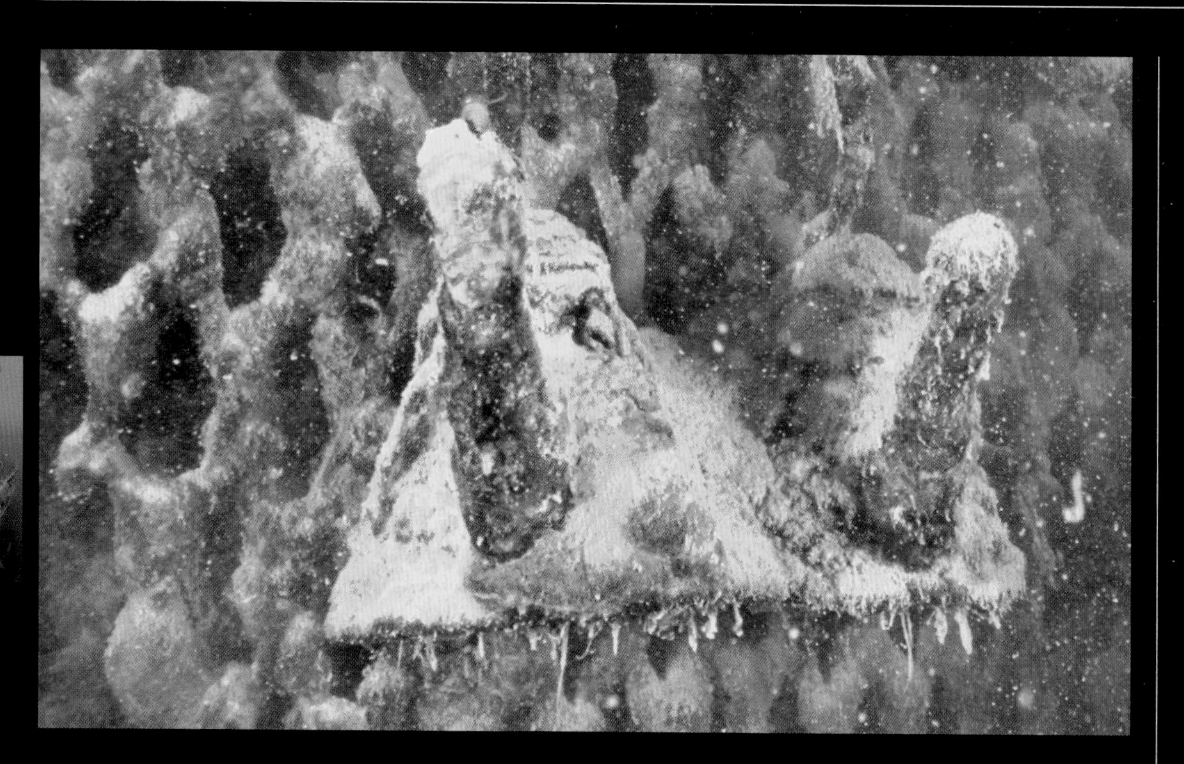

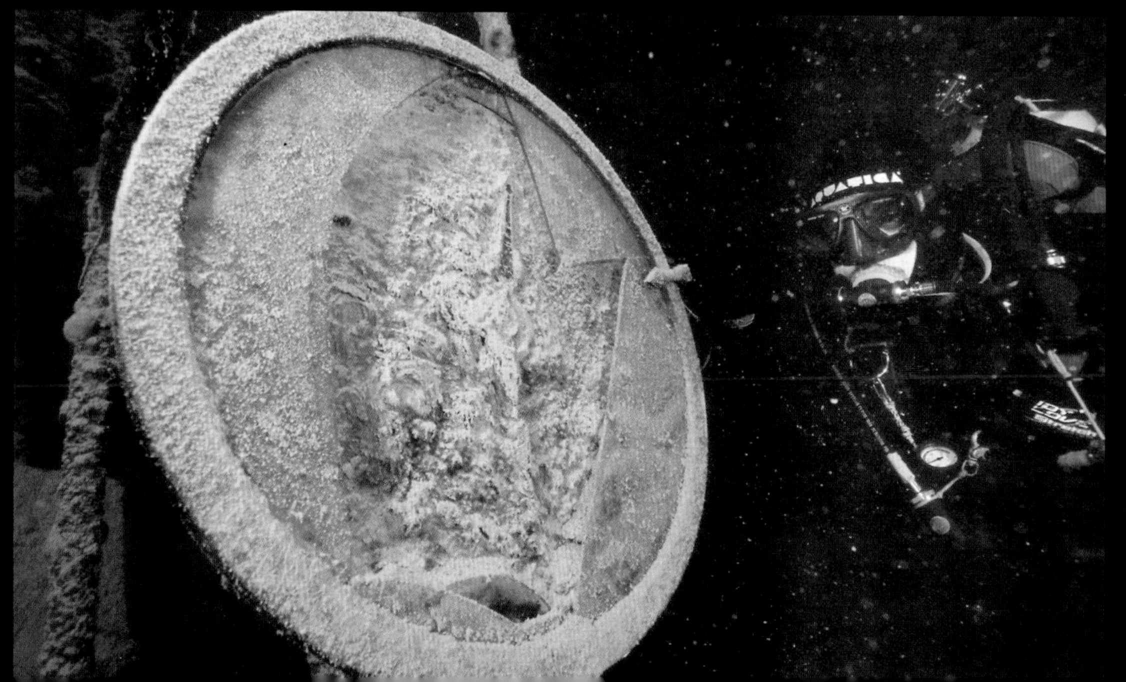

On the plate in the workshop of the engine room are still hanging the small oil cans

The engine room is situated at a depth of 46 meters and accommodates the 3-cylinder engine with triple expansion which was fuelled by two boilers. The predominant yellow-reddish colour is due to the mixed rust of fine muddy sediments which cover every structure. Pipes, wheelworks, flywheels, valves: everything has been perfectly conserved.

In the engine room you can still see the telegraph that used to transmit the captain's orders to the operators

AN EXPEDITION TO THE WRECK

In February 2003, an expedition explored the wreck thoroughly and systematically for the first time, taking a series of pictures and shooting over 60 hours of footage.
Stefano Zaffonato, a member of the expedition and its video-cameraman, gives his impressions: "Touring the wreck of the Rosalie Moller *was a fantastic experience for me.*
Seeing and exploring the ship that's considered 'the sister of the Thistlegorm,*' diving to between –35 and –52 meters with various mixtures that allowed us to stay submerged for a long time with a large safety margin wasn't easy but it wasn't impossible either.*
Our group, consisting of 15 scuba divers specialized in technical submersions, met up at the tourist center at El-Gouna, some twenty kilometers north of Hurghada.
There, TGI Diving *supplied the necessary technical assistance and made available a 25-meter boat to transport the 80 tanks needed for the expedition. We dove down with a double-tank of 15+15 liters with 26% nitrox, to which we had added, attached sideways, a 10-liter tank with 50% nitrox for the decompression.*
The three groups of 5 people each stayed submerged for a total of roughly 230 hours in complete safety. Seeing the captain's bathtub, the kitchen with its pots, the sinks on the floor (which were originally pink), the engine room complete with the light bulbs still intact, and the workshop with all the wrenches hanging up was an exciting experience we'll always remember. Add to that the good visibility and the rich fauna in the Red Sea and we couldn't fail to be thrilled."

Before submerging, scuba divers plan out each dive down to the smallest detail

On the Rosalie Moller's *bow, a member of the expedition puts a reserve tank in place to resurface*

until the autumn of 2000, when it was pulled off by the boats of divers who had used it as a mooring point; it now lies on the deck.
The gash caused by the bombs can be seen on the starboard side, just a few meters from the stern.
The fauna that lives in the wreck includes large groupers (*Epinephelus summana, E. tukula*) especially present in the bow, while lionfish (*Pterois miles*) and common bigeyes (*Priacanthus hamrur*) can be seen on the deck toward the stern. Glassfish (*Parapriacanthus ransonneti*), cave sweepers (*Pempheris vanicolensis*), pullers (genus *Chromis*) and large trevallies are to be found swimming throughout the whole ship.
The wreck of the *Rosalie Moller* is much less visited than that of the *Thistlegorm*, both because it is relatively far from the two main northern Red Sea resorts, Sharm el-Sheikh and Hurghada, and because it is more difficult to explore, due to the greater depth at which the vessel lies and the meteorological conditions (wind, waves, current) that generally prevail in this stretch of the sea.
As a result, the wreck is well-conserved and its structures are far less damaged than those of the *Thistlegorm*. Nonetheless, the number of scuba divers visiting the *Rosalie Moller* is on the increase, and the irreparable damage recently caused to the ship's funnel should encourage a greater sense of responsibility in potential visitors to the wreck.

The funnel of the Rosalie Moller with the letter M, the initial of the shipping company has been destroyed by a diving boat which used it as a mooring

*One of the numerous Common lionfish (*Pterois miles*) cruising around the hull*

The following organizations and archives have provided historic photographs, documents, facts, and information:
Lloyds of London - London
Imperial War Museum - London
Museum in the Docklands - London
National Maritime Museum - London
Newcastle Discovery Museum - Newcastle upon Tyne
National Geographic Society - Washington
British Library - London

In just a few years, wrecks are transformed into coral gardens

PHOTOGRAPH CREDITS

CLAUDIO BERTASINI: backcover; pages 5; 14–15; 35 above right; 38 above right; 39 above; 42 above left; 52–53; 60. MANFRED BORTOLI: pages 2–3; 4; 11 above left; 25 right; 28 above; 29 below; 32–33; 35 above left; 38 above left and below; 41 above and center; 42 above right; 51; 54–55; 56 left; 61 above left; 84. CLAUDIO CANGINI: pages 58; 59; 61above right. FABIO CASAROTTI: pages 34 right; 40 above; 41 below; 42 below; 48 below. FRANCESCO CHEMELLO: pages 62–63; 82 below. ARNAUD CHICUREL: pages 25 left; 57. FEDERICO FORLETTA: page 35 below. ALESSANDRO NORO: page 82 above. VINCENZO PAOLILLO: pages 8–9; 10; 11 below; 29 above; 29; 36–37; 40 below; 49; 65; 72 above left and below left; 74. ROBERTO RINALDI: pages 1; 11 right; 24 below; 28 below; 30–31; 39 below; 44–45; 68–69; 75; 76; 77; 78; 78–79; 80; 81; 83. ALBERTO SILIOTTI: pages 6–7; 24 above; 61 below right; 67. STEFANO ZAFFONATO: pages 72–73.

DRAWINGS

STEFANIA COSSU: pages 13; 19; 25; 26–27; 41; 46–47; 54–55; 66; 67; 70–71.
GIOVANNI PAULLI: 1st, 2nd, and 3rd of cover.
STEFANO TRAINITO: pages 32–33; 34; 35; 36; 43; 50; 72–73.